G000277835

JOHNNY
MNEMONIC

by the same author

BURNING CHROME

COUNT ZERO

MONA LISA OVERDRIVE

THE DIFFERENCE ENGINE (with Bruce Sterling)

VIRTUAL LIGHT

JOHNNY MNEMONIC

William Gibson

HarperCollins*Publishers*

HarperCollinsPublishers
77-85 Fulham Palace Road
Hammersmith, London W6 8JB

Published by HarperCollinsPublishers 1996

Copyright © CineVisions 1996
'Johnny Mnemonic' © William Gibson 1986

Plates section – Photographer: Takashi Seida. © 1995
ANM (1991) XXXIII Limited Partnership

The Author asserts his moral rights

A catalogue record for this book is
available from the British Library

ISBN   0 00 224618 X
0 00 648045 4 (Trade Paperback)

Set in Berkeley

Printed in Great Britain by
Scotprint Ltd, Musselburgh, Scotland

All rights reserved. No part of this publication may
be reproduced, stored in a retrieval system, or transmitted,
in any form or by any means, electronic, mechanical,
photocopying, recording or otherwise, without the prior
permission of the publishers.

The Screenplay

CREDITS BEGIN ON BLACK.

FADE UP MUSIC. Slowly, images start to bleed through. Red swirls, white, black dots . . . As more and more of the image bleeds through the titles we begin to make out what we're watching . . .

EXTERIOR. BEIJING. NIGHT.

EXTREME HIGH ANGLE traveling over an emotional demonstration approaching a solid line of SHIELDED RIOT POLICE. *Many of the* PARTICIPANTS *wear surgical masks and lab coats. The black dots identify themselves as their heads, the red-and-white swirls as banners they are carrying, mostly with Chinese lettering, but some in English as well as other languages. "CURE N.A.S. NOW."*

CAPTION: BEIJING, 2021.

Bellowing through BULLHORNS, pounding STEEL DRUMS, mouths screaming slogans behind surgical masks, but all the noise seems filtered, as if it's reaching us through some kind of aural barrier.

A number of the demonstrators suffer from NAS (Nerve Attenuation Syndrome), which manifests itself as a crippling palsy. Wild, angry eyes, twitching limbs.

Traffic is gridlocked. Drivers HONKING their horns inside their futuristic cars as the demonstration pours through.

We move in on a taxi, hopelessly stuck in the chaos . . .

JOHNNY (*voice-over*): I'm here.

RALFI   (*VO*): Did you get it?

JOHNNY   (*VO, casually*): Sure . . .

We are now close on the taxi and look inside . . .

INTERIOR. TAXI. NIGHT.

*RALFI's face on the vid-phone monitor inside. Deceptively chis-
eled features, long stringy hair and a sharp suit. He's JOHNNY's
agent for this job. Slightly nervous.*

RALFI: This is a big one, Johnny, you sure you can carry it? I could
send this new guy, who's fitted out with the latest . . .

ON JOHNNY.

*Young, sharply groomed, a conservative dark suit with white
shirt and tie, a bit too cool almost. Charming, confident, slick.
He seems supremely at ease. He's playing with a MATCHBOOK
in his hand. The DRIVER is getting increasingly nervous as
demonstrators surround the taxi, peer inside. Johnny ignores
the commotion.*

JOHNNY: Ralfi, stop worrying. I got upgraded with the MDA-18 this
morning . . .

*The demonstrators are SHOUTING. Some of them begin to
rock the taxi back and forth, trying to topple it. The driver
waves at them to go away, SHOUTS back in Chinese.*

JOHNNY: . . . You don't have a thing to worry about. It's under
control.

*Johnny hangs up, hands a few bills to the driver and unlocks
the door.*

JOHNNY: I'll walk.

He takes his briefcase and opens the door. For the first time, the NOISE hits us FULL BLAST.

EXT. TRAFFIC JAM. NIGHT.

The NOISE is scary, the anger palpable. Johnny, smiling benignly at the crowd, calmly creates a path through the mob; his calm benevolent expression and unhurried manner cause most people to give way to him. Johnny nods his thanks as he goes.

His luck doesn't last. One DEMONSTRATOR blocks his way, SCREAMING through his surgical mask. Johnny tries to go around. The demonstrator blocks him, still SHOUTING. Johnny smoothly ducks out of the way and jumps onto the hood of a car and over, blends into the crowd, smoothly, very fast.

EXT. DEMONSTRATION. NIGHT.

Johnny emerges from the thick of the crowd and pulls up short. The front of the demonstration has reached the riot police and the battle has been joined. Johnny turns and joins the running masses, his eyes looking for escape.

The riot police wade into the mass of panicked people. A CHINESE GIRL next to Johnny trips and falls. She SCREAMS. Johnny pauses, helps her up. She grabs him as if he is a life vest, hanging on, still SCREAMING.

The riot police are upon them, stream past. Johnny whirls the girl and himself to the side, out of the street. A COP charges them. Johnny blocks a swing from his club with his briefcase. The cop charges past.

The next COP resents Johnny blocking his colleague's swing and grabs him by the collar. Johnny brings up a small tube from his pocket, like a breath spray in appearance. In one fast movement he inserts it under the cop's Lucite mask and presses the spray button. The cop's mask turns white and wet with mist. He grabs for his eyes, HOWLING in pain, lets go of Johnny. Johnny looks around him. The Chinese girl has disappeared. Johnny heads for the edge of the masses.

EXT. STREET. NIGHT.

Johnny emerges from the crowd, stops, catches his breath. Looks down the street. Up ahead, a futuristic high-rise, a Chinese logo over the entrance. Johnny retrieves the book of matches from his pocket, opens it. Inside the cover, handprinted: #2571. He starts toward the tower.

EXT. BEIJING. NIGHT.

Beijing shimmers in the cold night air. We move back until we realize we're seeing the view from a hotel suite. Two men are looking out the windows and converse anxiously.

INT. HOTEL SUITE. NIGHT.

The two men are VIETNAMESE SCIENTISTS, huddled together. Small, frail-looking men in cheap suits. VIET #1 reaches to partially close the venetian blinds.

VIET #2:   The courier is late . . .

VIET #1:   Be calm.

While they are talking we move farther back into the room, revealing FOUR KOREAN BODYGUARDS. KOREAN #1 is enormously fat, like a sumo wrestler gone to seed. He puts back an empty plate next to a MINIATURE GRILL, still burning, on the coffee table. KOREAN #2, a body builder, is channel surfing, finally settles on a hyper-violent Japanese cartoon on TV. KOREAN #3, *a woman, chain-smokes while she cleans her automatic.* KO-REAN #4, *a cool fashion plate, isn't paying much attention to anything.*

VIET #2: We should have put it out on the global net while there was still time.

VIET #1: No. They're monitoring every fragment of transmitted data. A courier is the only way.

VIET #2: So we hire a criminal, with a silicon chip in his head—

VIET #1: A highly skilled smuggler. She chose him. As she chose us. You must remember that.

VIET #2: He's late.

VIET #1: Americans have a different sense of time . . .

INT. HOTEL LOBBY. NIGHT.

Grand and opulent. AFFLUENT GUESTS *mill about as if the world outside doesn't exist. An* ORIENTAL BAND *plays an Ink Spots tune on a small stage.*

Johnny enters the lobby, his suit in place and hair combed, and walks past a BANK OF VIDEO SCREENS. Most of the monitors are showing riot coverage, but all channels are a SPEED BARRAGE of images. Johnny joins a MAN *who, in his best tourist mode, is studying a map next to a potted fern. Following exchange in MANDARIN, subtitles, except Johnny's last line and the words "Pemex" and "MDA-18."*

JOHNNY: You have it?

The man is nervous.

MAN: I couldn't get one.

Johnny looks away in disgust. Anger building.

MAN   (*hurriedly*): They had a Pemex doubler . . . The guy said that should give you nearly the same capacity as the MDA-18.

JOHNNY: Not even close . . . (*sighs*) But it'll have to do.

The man hands over a small package, which Johnny slips into his pocket. He moves on.

Suddenly, on the monitors, the images start to skate and then are RIPPED open by a hand. J-BONE's computer-altered face (his eyes are pinpoints, his mouth is huge) appears on all the monitors. The cadence of his words is like an angry hip-hop hybrid.

J-BONE: Snatch back your brain, zombies! Snatch it back and hold it.

J-Bone's face changes again. For a brief moment, we see his undistorted face. He LAUGHS. THE MOVING LOGO of a DOL-PHIN (JONES) appears on the screen. The sound of dolphin SQUEAKS. The image is dramatically quiet compared to the barrage of images that make up contemporary TV.

The REACTIONS of the crowd suggest this is not an unusual disturbance. They're annoyed, resigned, amused.

Johnny heads for the elevators. A CHILD's face pops over the back of a couch. Johnny stops in his tracks, next to a large fishbowl. For a brief moment, he seems frozen, something going on inside his head he has no control over. Then it's over.

He takes a step back, so his head is behind the fishbowl, grossly distorted by the glass and the water. Grimaces at the kid. Brings up his hand, waves with curling fingers, like an octopus. The child beams.

CHILD: Again.

But Johnny's playfulness has disappeared as fast as it came and he's already moved on to the elevator bank.

INT. STRETCH LIMO. NIGHT.

In the streets near the hotel. SHINJI, a young, half-Japanese, half-American, fast-track Yakuza yuppie, cool and analytical, long hair in a ponytail, sits in the center. Checks his watch.

FOUR other impeccably dressed "businessmen" and ONE "businesswoman" around him, all of them impassive, but tense as they are stuck solid in the riot traffic. Heading for a "gig," the traffic jam fraying their nerves.

INT. ELEVATOR. NIGHT.

Johnny opens the package. The Pemex doubler is narrow, flat, has a DIGITAL COUNTER DISPLAY on its side. He peels back his hair, exposing JACK behind his ear. Inserts PROBE TIP of doubler, causing a slight involuntary spasm. Numbers DE-CREASE on counter as elevator floor-numbers INCREASE. He's relieved when it's done, disposes of used doubler, composes himself.

INT. HOTEL SUITE. NIGHT.

Image of riots on the TV. Korean #1 grunts, flicks the remote, the Japanese cartoon reappears. Door CHIMES. The Koreans whip out their guns. Koreans #2 and #3 answer it. Johnny's there, holding his briefcase like a pizza box.

JOHNNY: Double cheese, anchovies?

Viet #2 waves the Koreans out of Johnny's way. Johnny steps into the room, ignoring the Koreans, and, carefully sensing *the energy in the suite, crosses to a desk. Takes in the scene with his eyes. On edge.*

VIET #2:   You are Mr.—?

JOHNNY: Smith.

VIET #1:   You are late . . .

JOHNNY: Right . . .

Johnny senses the fear in the room. He steps around Korean #3 as if she's furniture. He pushes a button. The blinds rotate, lock: bars of red neon glare paint the walls. He waves cigarette smoke away with his hand. Another button starts the over-head fans.

JOHNNY: Question.

VIET #1:   Yes?

Another button, dimming the lights. The Koreans are bothered. He ignores them, turns to Viets.

JOHNNY: You don't look like the kind of people I usually work for . . . .

VIET #1:   We are . . . new at this.

JOHNNY: No shit. *Them* . . . (*indicates the Koreans*) . . . you coulda got out of a vending machine. *You* . . .

Viet #2's nerves are reaching the breaking point. The words stumble out.

VIET #2:   Please. We approached you through the correct channels. We paid half in advance into the Swiss account, exactly as your agent instructed—

JOHNNY: Yeah... What I'm saying is ... I was expecting *players.* You look like ... missionaries.

Viet #2 holds up an envelope; his hand is trembling.

VIET #2: Please! Everything is taken care of. Here's your ticket! First class!

BEAT.

JOHNNY: Let's see what you wanna upload.

Viet #1 hurriedly produces a manila envelope. Johnny goes over to the door, double locks it. Takes a MOTION DETECTOR from his briefcase, sticks it on the door frame. He does quick test, it BEEPS.

JOHNNY: Motion detector. In case the natives get restless ...

Viet #1 opens the envelope, extracts a small black case, opens it, revealing a dime-sized CD-ROM.

JOHNNY: How much am I carrying?

Viet #1 frowns. Johnny arms the motion detector. A BEEP and a red light starts pulsing. Johnny checks a small device on his belt. Another red light pulses in unison.

VIET #1: 320 gigabytes.

ON JOHNNY.

It's way too much but he's paying no attention.

JOHNNY: *Megabytes?*

VIET #2: Gigabytes.

VIET #2:   Your storage capacity—

JOHNNY: Where am I taking it?

VIET #1:   Newark.

Johnny's face falls.

VIET #2:   Your storage capacity—

JOHNNY   (*automatic bullshit*): *More* than adequate.

VIET #2:   It's extremely dangerous, if the upload volume exceeds your storage capacity. Synaptic seepage will kill you in two or three days, plus the data may be corrupted and a coherent download will be impossible . . .

Johnny realizes he may have a problem; we can see him doing the math in his head, figuring the odds, making his snap decision.

JOHNNY: I don't have a problem with that, okay? (*BEAT*) Are we loading or not?

VIET #2:   Your ticket . . .

VIET #2:   Your agent in Newark will arrange the meet for the download.

Viet #1 hands over an envelope.

JOHNNY: Perfect.

Johnny pockets ticket.

The Viets look at one another, silent agreement: no other choice. Johnny takes an assortment of objects from his brief-case, lining them up on the table near the window: roll of

Lifesavers, a credit card, a pair of sunglasses in a hard black case. The Viets and Koreans stare uncomprehendingly.

Johnny sits at the table.

CLOSE ON HIS HANDS.

As if performing a conjuring trick, he constructs the UPLOAD DEVICE from these materials. The final step involves a pair of fine gold cables; one snaps into the frame of his glasses, the other plugs into the JACK behind his ear. Both cables are then plugged into the upload device. Johnny hands UPLOAD RE-MOTE to Viet #1; a small pistol-like unit. This has several functions: it works like an ordinary TV remote; it can optically SCAN IMAGES off a TV screen; it TRANSMITS images to up-load unit via INFRARED PULSES, has a COUNTER.

JOHNNY: When the counter approaches zero, click on three frames of the TV. Any three. They'll meld with your data and I won't know what they are. That's the *download code.* You get a hard copy. You fax one copy to your connection on the other side . . .

He points over to the FAX MACHINE on the table.

JOHNNY: . . . When I get there, we feed in the code and download, delivery done. Understand?

Viet #1 looks at the remote. Nods. Johnny indicates a button on the upload device.

JOHNNY: Press that to start the upload.

Johnny puts some eyedrops in his eyes, puts on the sun-glasses, about to make a mistake that may cost him his life. Viet #2, hands trembling, slots the CD in the uploader.

JOHNNY: *Hit me.*

> *He pops a TOOTH PROTECTOR into his mouth.*
>
> *CLOSE-UP of mini disc, spinning, speeding into a silvery blur.*

INT. HOTEL LOBBY. NIGHT.

> *Shinji leads his team into the lobby.*
>
> *Incongruously, all of them, except for Shinji, are carrying gym bags. We may hear a soft CLANGING sound as one of the bags brushes against one of the men's legs.*
>
> *Shinji directs two of his team to stay in the lobby and precedes the others to the elevator banks.*

INT. ELEVATOR BANK. NIGHT.

> *CLOSE ON SHINJI's HAND.*
>
> *As he presses the elevator button. We notice the top part of his right thumb is a metal cap.*
>
> *HENSON, an American Yakuza, Shinji's right-hand man, can barely contain his excitement.*

HENSON: These guys: they *Viet-ching* or what?

SHINJI: No. Scientists. R&D people from Pharmakom. Defectors . . . Tokyo wants the *data.* Remember that.

> *Shinji stares at him; Henson gets the message. The DATA. The elevator arrives and they file in.*

INT. HOTEL SUITE. NIGHT.

> *DATA-STORM. An ultra-high-band-width barrage of visual data: an overpowering ultra-high-speed slit-scan barrage of*

formulas, moving molecule constructs, technical models, diagrams, etc., coming right at us. Mainlining cyberspace.

Johnny's body JERKS, his knuckles white on the arms of the chair. He GROANS, an unconscious sound. Whatever's happening to him, it isn't nice.

Viets #1 and #2 watch anxiously as he shivers under the constant psychic impact; he's jammed back, tight-jawed, in the chair. His face distorts in pain.

Viet #1 glancing constantly from the counter to Johnny.

The bodyguards are watching the Japanese cartoon again, sound off. They steal side glances at Johnny, pretending they're too jaded to care what's going on.

As the COUNTER approaches ZERO, Viet #1 crosses to TV, UPLOAD REMOTE in hand.

He triggers UPLOAD REMOTE by accident, capturing a freeze frame from the Japanese cartoon, the CARTOON HERO. The unit on the table BLEEPS as the image is recorded.

Johnny JERKS at the bleep, as the image is recorded on the chip in his brain. (We see the image burn through Johnny's point of view in the data-storm.) ON VIET #1 switching channels for the SECOND IMAGE, which we don't see. Viet #1 registers AMAZEMENT as we CUT to television in time to see the face of ANNA morph out of some other image. Her eyes. Viet #1's eyes. CUT TO JOHNNY'S SHARP JERK as a THIRD IMAGE hits him. Then it's over. Something banal on the television.

VIET #1:   The access code. Three images.

The unit on the table extrudes a small faxlike color tryptic of the images, but we can't identify them. Viet #1 tears this off, leaves it on the table, facedown.

INT. ELEVATOR. NIGHT.

The "businessmen's" gym bags CLANG as they put them down. They are zipped open.

A QUICK SERIES OF SHOTS.

As the men extract high-tech, futuristic air guns, cartridges, SLAM the cartridges into place, check their bulletproof vests underneath their clothes and otherwise turn themselves into walking arsenals. Only Shinji stands calmly, seemingly unarmed.

INT. HOTEL SUITE. NIGHT.

Johnny SAGS as the barrage ends, white-faced behind the glasses.

VIET #2:   Mr. Smith?

Johnny pulls the glasses off. His eyes are closed. He opens them. Blinks. Looks up at Viet #2, his eyes scary and blank. He removes the gold cables and stuffs them in his pocket, moving as if he's on automatic pilot. Gets up. Unsteady on his feet. Conceals this, but a trickle of blood comes down his nostril.

JOHNNY: Where's the bathroom?

VIET #2:   What?

JOHNNY: The toilet.

Viet #2 points. Johnny walks through suite. The other rooms are dark, except for the bright white bathroom. He enters, closing door.

INT. HOTEL. CORRIDOR. NIGHT.

The elevator doors open. Shinji and his men walk out and down the hallway.

INT. HOTEL SUITE. BATHROOM. NIGHT.

Johnny convulses, holding his temples, face twisted with pain.

JOHNNY: Oh, Jesus, Jesus, *shit* . . .

He attempts to stabilize himself, holding HIS HANDS OUT IN FRONT OF HIM and BREATHING SLOWLY until they stop shaking. It is a meditative exercise we will see him do again later. He feels better. Looks at himself in mirror. Notices the blood. Wipes it off. Splashes water on his face.

INT. HOTEL. CORRIDOR. NIGHT.

While his men stand back, Shinji UNCAPS HIS THUMB and carefully extrudes a glittering LOOP of filament from his thumb-tip.

INT. HOTEL SUITE. HALLWAY. NIGHT.

Johnny hears a SOUND from the bedroom, notices the door ajar, moves over.

JOHNNY's *POV.*

Light from bathroom spills into the bedroom, illuminating the WIVES and CHILDREN of the defecting Viets, seated in a row along the edge of the bed. Eyes wide. Silent. Best Sunday clothes. Twenty-first-century Boat People. One WIFE is breast-feeding.

One YOUNG CHILD looks straight at him. His stare solemn.

ON JOHNNY.

For a flash moment (as when he saw the child in the lobby) it seems as if the scene strikes a chord deep inside him. Johnny seems woozy, puts a hand against the wall to support himself.

A soft BUZZ. Johnny checks his belt. The motion detector is going off. Johnny glances at the suite door. The LED there is shining solid red. He takes a step back into the bathroom, kills the light.

INT. HOTEL SUITE. NIGHT.

QUICK SHOTS: The Koreans, on the couch, are engrossed in the Japanese cartoon. The SOUND is back ON.

Viet #2 turns on a FAX machine, holding the code images to send out.

Viet #1 is toasting the micro-CD over the cooker, holding it in the steel chopsticks.

INT. HOTEL. CORRIDOR. NIGHT.

Shinji and his men square themselves off, exchange looks Shinji nods. WHIPS the filament-loop down, toward the door-knob.

INT. HOTEL SUITE. NIGHT.

CLOSE ON THE TV.

A hyperkinetic explosion of Japanese cartoon-blood.

ON THE DOOR.

As the loop pops through it like a knife through butter, scooping out the knob and lock.

CLOSE ON THE MICRO-CD.

In the steel chopsticks; it's sagging, starting to melt.

YAKUZAS #1 and #2 burst through the door, followed by Henson.

QUICK CUT surreal slaughter scene as Shinji's men overwhelm the Korean bodyguards. (Note: The Yakuza are armed with sophisticated, relatively silent air guns, the Koreans with traditional ballistic guns).

Yakuza #1 shoots Korean #1 as he's rising from the sofa, attempting to draw a massive folding-stock automatic. Korean #1 is blown across the room, crashing into the blinds. Korean #1's gun strafes a trail of bullets across the ceiling as he falls.

Yakuza #2 blows away Korean #3, who tries to take shelter behind one of the pillars.

Henson turns left toward the bathroom and the bedroom, advances. The bathroom door is open, dark inside . . .

Korean #4 hits Yakuza #2 with a salvo. The bullets bounce harmlessly off the Yakuza's bulletproof vest. For a moment, the Korean stands in shock, then he dives behind the sofa. Yakuza #2 riddles the sofa with bullets. Stuffing flies. Korean #4's wrist flops out from behind the sofa, remains motionless.

Henson reaches the bathroom, enters cautiously. He reaches for the light switch, flips it. Johnny SLAMS the door closed into his head and on his wrist, immediately pulls it open again, wrenches the dazed Henson inside and SLAMS him through the GLASS SHOWER DOORS.

CLOSE ON THE MICRO-CD.

Falling into cooker as Viet #2 lets go of it. He crouches down, fatalistically waiting to be shot.

Johnny appears in the doorway, sizes up the situation in an instant. His eyes take in the access code. The doorway.

Shinji notices Johnny, moves forward.

CLOSE ON THE ACCESS CODE.

Slowly being pulled into the fax machine.

Viet #2 notices Johnny is heading for the table, understands immediately. He steps toward Johnny.

Johnny lunges forward, but Shinji's filament sings through the air. Johnny snatches the paper from the fax machine, just as the filament cuts through it. He's left holding only a single image. There's no time for more. The filament also cuts through a stone statue in its lethal path.

Johnny dives for the door and rolls. He's very fast. The next moment he's gone. Behind him, the wall is STRAFED with bullets.

Yakuzas #1 and #2 sprint after him, blocking Shinji's target.

Viet #2 has picked up the remaining code images and reaches for the flames in the cooker, but Shinji whips his filament and severs his hand, which falls right on the edge of the cooker, still clutching the code. The flames reach for the paper, quickly singeing one side.

Shinji lunges for the paper, grabs it before it's completely consumed. One-half (one of the two remaining images) has been destroyed. Shinji is furious. He grabs the lone survivor, horrified Viet #1. All the others in the room are dead.

SHINJI: You. Where's he going? Where's he taking the data?

Viet #1 is too scared to speak.

In the next room, a baby begins to CRY. A slow smile spreads across Shinji's face.

INT. FIRE STAIRS. NIGHT.

Johnny races down the steps. He jumps over the railing onto the next landing and keeps running. In the process, he re-

verses his tie, runs his hands through his hair, gray streaks appear. He takes a folded hat from his pocket, pushes it out, gradually transforming himself. Takes out a small square package, snaps it; it unfolds into a raincoat. He pops a pill into his mouth.

ON HIS HAND . . .

. . . as it reaches for the balustrade to swing himself around a corner. The skin tone is changing before our eyes.

RUNNING STEPS on the stairs above him . . .

INT. HOTEL LOBBY. NIGHT.

An Oriental traveling salesman, his gait stiff, his shoulders sloped, emerges into the lobby. Shinji's guards don't even give him a second look as he walks straight through the lobby and out the door.

Only the child for whom he did the little trick in the lobby, when he came in, stares after him, puzzled. On the brink of recognition.

Just as Johnny walks out, the trailing Yakuza explode into the lobby. Shinji's guards immediately converge. They stand there, looking around uncertainly.

The child looks over to the Yakuza, frowning. He doesn't like them.

EXT. NEWARK. NIGHT.

ESTABLISHING SHOT of the city. Many areas are completely dark. As if deserted. Very different from futuristic and bustling Beijing.

CAPTION: FREE CITY OF NEWARK.

INT. NEWARK AIRPORT. CUSTOMS. NIGHT.

A SERIES OF MRI IMAGES.

Scanning through a human body. OVER THIS: airport sounds, FLIGHT ANNOUNCEMENTS, etc.

A CUSTOMS OFFICER, Hispanic, looks at the monitor as the ARRIVALS file through his booth, each head and body very much the same. Suddenly, one head is different, an IMPLANT shows, something angular and inorganic in the brain. An ALARM sounds.

Johnny stops and looks over to the Customs Officer.

JOHNNY: It's all right, it's government approved. Dyslexia prosthesis.

He hands over a laminated card. The Customs Officer reads it, punches in the number. Looks back up to Johnny, suspicious . . . checks his monitor. Back at Johnny. For a moment we think Johnny's blown. BEAT.

CUSTOMS OFFICER: You may have a problem here . . . Looks like your implant is discharging . . . seepage. Better get it checked immediately.

JOHNNY: *Gracias.*

Gets a grin from Customs Officer.

Johnny takes back his card and moves on, turns the corner of a bare corridor. Image BURNS OUT into . . .

INT. TAKAHASHI'S APARTMENT. DAUGHTER'S ROOM. NIGHT.

THE FACE OF TAKAHASHI.

Impeccably attired in the conservative suit of the Japanese "company man." He is the Yakuza head for this sector of North America.

Stoical and melancholy, he's like a Roman legionnaire holding down the fort in Wales; he may be a gangster, but in a sense he's the law in this neck of the woods.

He sits on a huge pink powder puff of a bed, an incongruous presence in what appears to be the room of a very wealthy twenty-first-century child. Everything here is intelligent, highly interactive, fawningly user-friendly. A black-draped Shinto shrine strikes a false note.

Takahashi is watching . . .

His eight-year-old daughter, MIKIYO, *play in a pool of light in the corner of the room. Her back is half turned, her short black hair making a neat line against her white neck. His concentration is completely on her game.*

MIKIYO   (*addressing a doll*): Now, Mopmop, if you and Shirley can't play nicely, I'm going to have to separate you.

Takahashi remains expressionless, but there is a sad tenderness in his eyes that contrasts with the evident hardness of his features. A KNOCK on the door. As if caught at something, Takahashi quickly pushes a button on a hand-held remote. His daughter DISSOLVES AND VANISHES . . .

She was a hologram all along . . .

The door opens, spilling a shaft of light across the bed. His SECRETARY *enters.*

SECRETARY: Sorry to disturb you, Mr. Takahashi . . .

TAKAHASHI   (*grimly*): . . . Shinji has arrived.

He gets up and exits the room.

EXT. FORMAL JAPANESE GARDEN/OFFICE. NIGHT.

Takahashi's office is open to a covered indoor Japanese formal garden. Shinji executes a negligent, almost insolent bow as Takahashi enters. Takahashi nods and walks to his desk.

TAKAHASHI: You look well. Asia agrees with you.

He looks at Shinji's capped thumb, smiles contemptuously.

TAKAHASHI: I see you have found a way to turn your shame into an asset.

Shinji instinctively folds his thumb underneath his hand.

SHINJI   (*coldly*): My condolences, Takahashi-san, on your recent sad loss.

Takahashi switches to Japanese, as if he didn't hear Shinji.

TAKAHASHI: I've seen the report from Tokyo. Pharmakombinat Industrie of Zurich have engaged us to recover their missing data.

Shinji also switches to Japanese.

SHINJI: Our operation in Beijing met with limited success. The Pharmakom traitors are dead.

That is to say: a nearly complete failure.

TAKAHASHI   (*impassive*): And the mnemonic courier escaped. He is coming here?

SHINJI: We have reason to believe so.

TAKAHASHI: Why was I not informed at once?

SHINJI: I did not wish to disturb you in your time of grief. It must be terrible to lose a child, an only child, especially so young . . . I assumed you were . . . unavailable.

Shinji's sympathy is a deliberate torment, an attempt to cast blame on Takahashi.

TAKAHASHI: We are Yakuza. I am *always* available. What is the nature of the data?

SHINJI: I am not at liberty to say.

Takahashi smiles coldly.

TAKAHASHI: Because you do not know?

Direct hit.

SHINJI: I have been charged with recovering the head of the courier. Cryogenically preserved.

TAKAHASHI: Preserved?

SHINJI: The defectors wiped the Pharmakom mainframe. If we lose the courier, we've lost the data forever.

Takahashi switches to English.

TAKAHASHI: Newark is mine. You were insolent when you trained here under me and you have not changed. You will report to me. If the courier is in my territory, I will be responsible. I understand you obtained part of the courier's download code?

No reaction from Shinji.

TAKAHASHI: Give it to me.

Shinji deliberates, then shrugs, produces the singed piece of paper, hands it over, executes another of his insolent bows and leaves. Takahashi looks at the image. A frame of the RIOTS. He presses the intercom.

TAKAHASHI: Get me Karl Honig.

. *A pause. Takahashi's vid-phone clicks on. Sequence of generic Christian religious images.*

DEACONESS   (*VO*): Church of the Retransfiguration. Fax your tax-deductible contribution to . . .

The image furs with green static and is replaced by a "screen" on which we see J-Bone.

J-BONE: Make your *own* images and get your life *back*! The human race is waiting for *you* . . . !

J-Bone's image explodes into a fast-forward LOTEK VIDEO-SCRATCH, set to music. Takahashi is appalled. He flips the intercom switch.

TAKAHASHI: Our lines are triple-shielded, we have our own satellites and still my private line is invaded by these Lotek anarchists . . .

SECRETARY   (*offscreen*): I don't know how . . .

TAKAHASHI: Have the technicians in *immediately*.

Takahashi glowers at the Lotek video. It breaks up into static, the HISS filling the office.

INT. CAB. NIGHT.

Johnny in the back of a junker speeding through potholed back streets of Newark. The DRIVER is visibly nervous in this part of town.

Johnny, looking terrible, talks to Ralfi on an antique portable phone as he changes back from salesman to his usual self.

We INTERCUT the conversation with exteriors as the cab drives through the stark wasteland to its destination.

JOHNNY: I'm *way* overloaded, man. You wouldn't believe how much—

RALFI (*VO*): Johnny-boy, you *told* me you got upgraded.

JOHNNY: Yeah, yeah, I *did.* I got the goods, Ralfi. Now I just wanna get 'em out of my head! Did they get the code out?

RALFI (*VO*): Don't worry, Johnny-boy, they say they can extract, easy.

A huge relief. But Johnny doesn't betray it in his voice.

JOHNNY: "They" who? What's going on, Ralfi? This feels like a blown deal, man . . . I don't even know this shithole of a town, I'm gonna be completely exposed—

RALFI (*VO*): Johnny-boy, Johnny-boy, has Ralfi ever let you down? Delivery is confirmed. You say you have to get data out, they're the only ones who can do it. You have no choice.

JOHNNY: . . . Okay, I'll check this place out.

RALFI (*VO*): Be careful. Let's have a drink later, all right? Meet face-to-face, after all this time.

JOHNNY: Yeah, sure.

He breaks the connection. Takes out the single code image from his pocket. Looks at it. Frustrated. Worried.

CUT TO:

INT. DROME BAR. NIGHT.

Set in a plush, old, converted theater, this is one cooking joint, and about as weird as it gets—weirder, even.

Some very heavy customers, rough trade of every conceivable persuasion, plus a healthy leavening of latex-clad jailbait to die for. Some of the customers, though, are victims of Nerve Attenuation Syndrome (NAS). They jive and jitter, hard as they may try to be inconspicuous.

Ralfi is at the corner table that serves him as an office. He's a "talent agent" for various kinds of underworld professionals. PRETTY and YOMOMMA, a striking pair of female combat artists, flank him.

Yomomma is black, Pretty white and blond; otherwise they could have been built from the same kit: Superdeluxe Professional Ballcrusher. They work for Ralfi.

Ralfi hangs up the vid-phone, exchanges a glance with Pretty and Yomomma and lifts the phone again. Dials.

AT THE BAR.

SPIDER, a startling blend of computer geek and surfer/muscle builder with a pumped physique. He's very on edge, wears plain geeky glasses and is talking with JANE, who is sitting next to him: young, decidedly unprosperous, inexperienced. Local talent. A wannabe. She's taut and edgy, in skintight jeans and a leather jacket with the sleeves ripped out. Leans forward, hungry and intense. She keeps looking over at Ralfi's table.

SPIDER: About these *episodes* you've been having—I want to get you back to the shop for some tests . . . Hey! Are you even listening!?

JANE: We aren't playin' "doctor" anymore, remember?

SPIDER: Hey, that's not what I—

JANE: Look at them. The lap dancers from hell. They're *old*! I'm twice as fast as they are.

SPIDER: I'm not *worried* about your speed, I'm worried about your nervous system . . .

She isn't really listening; her attention is on Ralfi as he talks into his phone. As soon as he hangs up, she gets up and heads over to his table. Spider looks after her. Angry. Jealous.

AT THE TABLE.

Ralfi looks up as Jane struts up, concentrating on exuding street fighter charisma. Pretty moves to block Jane.

PRETTY: No *way*—

But Pretty's too-casual swing backfires. Jane intercepts it, spinning Pretty off balance: a very slick move. Ralfi's mouth is open; Jane is in his face.

JANE: Your hired muscle's aging on you, Ralfi. I coulda *done* ya. Time you hired some young and fast.

PRETTY   (*hissing with fury*): You—crazy—little—street—trash—bitch—

Ralfi studies her. Almost interested. He holds up his hand to Yomomma, keeping her off.

RALFI: Like you?

PRETTY: You gonna be shitting out of a plastic bag.

JANE   (*selling*): You agent for all the best combat artists in town. I'm the fastest thing going now Spider's jacked my system.

RALFI: You fast, huh? (*BEAT*) Hold out your hand.

Puts out his hand, flat, palm down, held about six inches above the table. Jane, thinking her speed is about to be tested somehow, pulls back her sleeve, makes a fist; CLOSE on her inner forearm, faint ruler-straight lines of scarification where Spider's worked on her. She puts out her hand as well.

JANE: Okay?

RALFI: Fine. Just hold it there.

Silence. He watches Jane's hand. We wait for something to happen.

JANE: So?

Ralfi's poker-faced.

JANE: *What?*

RALFI: Just hold it there.

Flash of fear in Jane.

RALFI: You can hold it there, baby . . . can't you?

JANE: Sh-sure . . .

CLOSE-UP ON Jane's hand as it starts to TREMBLE. Before the tremor can increase, she grabs Ralfi's wrist. She is fast.

JANE (*desperate*): See?

Ralfi stares at her coldly, until she lets go. Shakes his head. Yomomma laughs, cruelly.

YOMOMMA: You're damaged goods, bitch. Spider-man's jacked you up, all right.

PRETTY: Jacked her so tight, she shakes . . .

YOMOMMA: Another month or two, you'll be like them . . .

Pointing to trembling victims of NAS at the bar, beer slopping from one's glass as he tries to drink.

RALFI: I can't use you. Not for muscle. You could be kinda cute, though, somebody clean you up. Ever consider something a little less *actively* physical?

He absently sizes up her breasts, picking his teeth.

YOMOMMA: Yeah. Like *on your back*?

Pretty HOWLS with laughter.

PRETTY: Or on your knees!

Jane looks as if she could go ballistic, but she bottles it in. Stands up.

JANE: *I'll get a gig,* Ralfi.

He turns back to his laptop. Jane vanishes into the crowd around bar.

EXT. RATLANDS. NIGHT.

Ridge of landfill, trash blowing. Spooky. A CAB crests a ridge. The door opens and Johnny gets out. The cab immediately turns and takes off.

Johnny moves carefully in the direction of the factory, taking advantage of cover.

EXT. FACTORY. GIRDERS. NIGHT.

Squinting down through a monocular, J-Bone, the Lotek leader, watches Johnny. Wears a slightly more distinctive version of the Lotek costume, which runs to layers, ragged leggings, neck-thongs strung with tools and bits of high-tech junk. He has an AIR BOW slung across his back.

TOAD, thirteen, a young Lotek, comes strolling out on the girder behind him. But we're thirty feet up, here. Toad as casual as if he's goofing in the playground.

TOAD: Yo, J-Bone, maximum leader, sir. Watcha clockin'?

J-Bone's not pleased at being interrupted. He gestures for Toad to shut up. Indicates Johnny scurrying closer. Toad joins him. Squats next to him.

J-Bone raises the monocular to his eye again, watches Johnny as he approaches the ruins of an old building.

EXT. RATLANDS. NIGHT.

Ruins of a factory and outbuildings. Near a river, partially in the shadow of a BRIDGE.

Inside, a burnt shell of a building with blacked-out windows; a strip of light leaks under the warped door.

EXT. RATLANDS. NIGHT.

Johnny skirts the building, checking it out. Moves up to the door. Removes the motion detector from his belt, ATTACHES IT TO THE DOORJAMB. He bends over and tries to peer through the crack. The door opens inward, fast. Johnny's eyes level with LASLO's cowboy-booted ankles.

LASLO: You're Johnny.

JOHNNY   (*steps back*): Am I?

LASLO: Sure hope so. Come on in.

Laslo is a streetfighter, the kind of foot soldier the Yakuza tends to bring along for operations in these bad-ass anarcho parts of town. Johnny hesitates, suspicious.

Laslo smiles indulgently. He stands aside to let Johnny in. Johnny hesitantly steps in.

JOHNNY's *POV.*

Quick pan along the length of a table spread with white plastic. At the far end, a CRYO-UNIT, a patented head freezer. A GLITTERING array of surgical tools.

Henson, HEAVILY BANDAGED, wearing surgical gloves, steps forward. Smiles.

HENSON: Doctor will see you now.

Johnny calmly turns to Laslo, who is now blocking his way.

JOHNNY: You lied.

LASLO: Yeah . . .

Johnny's hand reaches for his watch, presses a button.

THE MOTION DETECTOR EXPLODES, right behind Laslo.

Johnny immediately headbutts Laslo, then grabs his arm and throws him forward across the table. Instruments flying. Laslo crashes to the ground.

Johnny dives out the door. Henson goes after him with a HIGH-TECH GUN with silencer, skeletal stock, telescopic laser sight.

EXT. RATLANDS. NIGHT.

Johnny ducks into rubble. Henson stalks him. He's good at this.

HENSON: We got all night, white meat.

TILT UP to where J-Bone and Toad look down, observing everything. Toad starts to speak; J-Bone claps palm across his mouth.

Johnny, hiding in the rubble below, picks up a length of rusty steel bar; hefts it in his hand.

Henson, turning slowly, is spooked when the steel rod crashes into a nearby pile of metal scrap. But it doesn't draw his fire, as Johnny had hoped it would.

Overhead, Toad's eyes are popping with excitement.

J-Bone, worried, gestures for Toad to keep quiet. Toad nods. But as Toad restlessly shifts his feet on the girder, he accidentally dislodges a scrap of concrete balanced there.

It lands near Henson, who whips the gun up and fires.

Overhead, Toad's been shot underneath his chin. He tries to reach up, loses his balance, tumbles to the ground, already dead.

J-BONE: *Toad!!!*

Toad crashes into the rubble. J-Bone runs back along girder, disregarding his own safety completely. He starts descending the structure.

Johnny watches from hiding. Henson checks Toad's body, nudges it with his shoe, resumes his search.

J-Bone runs to Toad's body. Kneels beside it, cradling the dead boy's head.

J-BONE: Toad, Toad, shit, man . . .

Looks up into the muzzle of Henson's gun, inches from his eye.

HENSON: You weren't on the menu, but I want you to do something for me . . .

J-BONE: Do?

HENSON: Yes. Say: "Bye" . . .

Henson's finger tightening on trigger. We hear a sound like someone slugging a watermelon with a baseball bat. Henson falls forward and we see Johnny with a length of waterlogged two-by-four in his hands. J-Bone looks up at him.

LASLO   (*OS*): Just hold it right there.

Johnny turns. Sees Laslo has the drop on them with an assault rifle. J-Bone smiles broadly at Laslo, lifts his arm. ZING. A small crossbow on his wrist releases a bolt. Laslo staggers, falls face-first in a puddle. J-Bone turns back to Toad.

Johnny picks up Henson's gun. Snaps off the laser sight and tosses it in a puddle. Then the silencer, then the stock. He's left with a squat, brutal-looking PISTOL. J-Bone watches.

J-BONE: You tooling up for an evening of it?

JOHNNY: If they think you're technical, go crude . . .

J-BONE: . . . If they think you're crude, go technical. Uh-huh. However you gonna go, you and I are even now, understand?

His look says Johnny won't get any favors. He scoops up the LASER SIGHT, shakes it dry, estimates its usefulness, stuffs it in a pocket.

JOHNNY: Who are you?

J-BONE: I'm J-Bone. I run Heaven. Up there.

He points to a bridge looming in the distance. For the first time we see, patched underneath, like an insect nest, a makeshift town, suspended underneath what once was the roadway across the river.

INT. TAKAHASHI'S OFFICE. NIGHT.

*Takahashi is at his desk, watching a HOME MOVIE of his WIFE
and his daughter on the wall screen. Suddenly, as the camera
MOVES IN on his daughter, she begins to transform. Sound of
MOZART gradually fills the room. Mikiyo turns into Anna, an
eerily beautiful young/old woman in a period costume. Candles burn. A blue, surreal world. Takahashi blinks.*

ANNA: How sad . . .

*He gets up, moves closer to the display. Anna's shape floats
forward down a seemingly endless corridor, flanked by classi-
cal archways until she arrives in close-up.*

TAKAHASHI: Who . . . what are you? This is not—

ANNA: So very sad, Mr. Takahashi. The loss of a child—

Takahashi takes vial of pills from jacket, swallows several.

TAKAHASHI: You are a phantasm! An hallucination!

ANNA: Then let us hallucinate *together*. There is a story I must tell
you. You will understand—

TAKAHASHI: No!

ANNA: Yes, I was *like* you, Takahashi. Rigid. My will flashing like
lightning between all the world's megacities. My name a cold
wind in the corridors of power.

TAKAHASHI: You are . . . sent by my enemies!

ANNA: I am sent by conscience. In the name of memory.

TAKAHASHI: Memory?

ANNA: Where I am, Takahashi, there is only . . . memory. Memory
and the play of conscience . . . an endless reckoning of the

score. If there was never such a thing as hell before, we surely invented it. But I see you there. I *know* you. Your purpose is lost. At the very core of all your power, there is only an emptiness . . . hollowness . . . carved in the shape of the absent child—

The door opens and Takahashi's secretary enters. Anna's world VANISHES, taking her with it, in a HIGH-SPEED REVERSE MORPH, leaving Takahashi looking dazed. His daughter again smiles out from the screen at him.

His secretary puts some papers in front of him.

SECRETARY: I still haven't reached Reverend Honig.

TAKAHASHI: Keep trying.

The secretary looks up, sees Takahashi's daughter on the screen. She hides her concern for him.

INT. DROME BAR. MEN'S ROOM. NIGHT.

Ralfi enters, goes to urinal. Just as he unzips, Johnny grabs him, SLAMMING him face-first into the wall. Holds him there, squashing his face against the tiles.

JOHNNY: They were waiting for me, Ralfi, two big, nasty men . . .

RALFI: Johnny-*boy*! Please! Let me go—

Johnny SLAMS his face into the tiles again. Puts the pistol to his head.

JOHNNY: You set me up, my *friend*!

RALFI: Johnny, it's not my fault, there's been a screwup, but it's not—

JOHNNY: Your ass is *dead* if you don't get this batch of product out of my—

Johnny is grabbed from behind and Yomomma hurls him headfirst against a steel cubicle door. Johnny crumples to the floor. Ralfi turns and freaks.

RALFI: Not on the *head*! Tell me you didn't hit him on the head!

Yomomma shrugs, looks around.

YOMOMMA: I haven't been in one of these in *years* . . .

RALFI   (*rubbing his cheek, furious*): Not since you had a dick, yes? Now get him into the back room.

Yomomma lifts Johnny up like a broken doll.

INT. DROME BAR. NIGHT.

AT THE BAR.

HOOKY, the ancient bartender, his skeletal prosthetic forearm ending in namesake hooked pincers, is serving Jane one on the house when Jane sees Yomomma carry Johnny's limp body into the back room. Her eyes narrow as she sees a YAKUZA GUARD position himself in front of the door.

INT. DROME BAR. BACK ROOM. NIGHT.

BLURRY POV.

Of the ceiling, slowly coming into focus. Ralfi's face appears.

RALFI   (*sympathetic*): How you feeling?

Johnny GROANS, tries to reach for his head. Finds he's tied down flat on his back on a table (his legs are free). His pistol lies useless next to his feet. Absorbs this. Remains calm.

JOHNNY   (*drowsy*): What'd they upload, Ralfi, the goddamn Library of Congress? My brain feels like it's gonna explode . . .

RALFI: I think your friend here, he can take care of that . . .

Shinji steps forward. He's wearing a cheap transparent rain-coat over his suit, buttoned to the neck.

Johnny stares, recognizing him, suddenly knowing he's not intended to leave the room alive.

JOHNNY   (*dragged by depth of betrayal*): Ralfi, you lying sack of shit!

RALFI: What am I supposed to do? Argue with the Yakuza? I'm not making a penny off of this.

Yakuza. Johnny takes a good look at Shinji as he hoists the CRYOGENIC STORAGE UNIT onto the tabletop.

Shinji picks up a length of surgical tubing with an arterial shunt on one end, like a half-inch-diameter hypodermic needle.

SHINJI: We'll need a bucket . . .

INT. DROME BAR. MEN'S ROOM. NIGHT.

Jane slips in, looks up at foam-tile-and-T-bar ceiling; hoists herself up a water pipe above urinals. Pushes a ventilation grid aside.

INT. DROME BAR. VENTILATION DUCT. NIGHT.

Pulls herself up and in.

INT. DROME BAR. BACK ROOM. NIGHT.

Johnny writhes, looking at the shunt as Pretty rummages among janitorial supplies, finding a filthy five-gallon bucket.

PRETTY: Well, it's not sterile . . .

SHINJI: It will do. Put it there, beside the table . . .

JOHNNY: Can't we talk about this?

SHINJI: Talk?

JOHNNY: I have one image of the access code, you have the other
two. I'll give you the data, everybody happy.

BEAT. Shinji twiddling the shunt.

SHINJI: No. You don't understand. They don't just want the data.
They want everything it's ever been stored in.

*It dawns on Johnny that Shinji is talking about cutting off his
head. His eyes widen as he looks at the cryo-unit with full
understanding of its purpose.*

SHINJI: There's less danger of information decay. And we don't
have to worry about anyone going in with advanced sensor
technology . . . These days, you see, dead men can tell tales.

*Shinji puts the shunt down, goes to the unit, snaps it open. Puff
of super-chilled air. Clicks cryo-unit shut.*

JOHNNY: There's gotta be a way to work this out—

SHINJI: There is.

*He takes a small rubber ball, puts it in Johnny's mouth, gagging
him. He rounds the table, picking up shunt.*

INT. DROME BAR. VENTILATION DUCT. NIGHT.

*JANE's POV through a small grate, watching, braced in an
awkward position. Under her weight, the welded joint of the
ducts is beginning to sag. She shifts her weight.*

INT. DROME BAR. BACK ROOM. NIGHT.

Shinji pulls down a plasticine mask over his face, examines the razor edged point of the shunt. Checks to make sure the rubber tube is in the bucket.

YOMOMMA: Will you hurry up?! This is kinda disgusting, you stop to think about it . . .

Shinji smiles. He traces the line of the artery in Johnny's neck with one finger . . .

INT. DROME BAR. VENTILATION DUCT. NIGHT.

Jane is horrified by the spectacle. She tests the joint beneath her, makes a decision, draws her knees to her chest and drops her weight full onto the joint, which immediately gives way.

INT. DROME BAR. BACK ROOM. NIGHT.

She lands on the table in a shower of dust. A section of pipe swings down, sending Shinji sprawling, stunning him.

RALFI: What the fuck . . . ?

Pretty goes for Jane and gets a very solid, very expert kick in the head. Pretty goes down.

Yomomma puts an expensive-looking SPRING-KNIFE to Johnny's neck. The blade SNAPS OUT, right on the button for Johnny's jugular.

Jane counters instantly, flipping out her own WEAPON: a telescoping car-antenna with a nasty fang of steel welded at the tip. The blade bobs, CU, like the tip of a fly rod in front of Yomomma's face.

Yomomma stiffens.

YOMOMMA: I'll slit his fucking throat, bitch.

Jane stops. Cocks her head.

JANE: So? Other guy gonna cut his whole head off.

Johnny's eyes are fixed on Jane, as if he sees his way out of here.

Shinji's on his hands and knees, getting his bearings.

Ralfi absently mops his forehead.

RALFI: Jane-Jane, what say we pay you for a night's work and you just walk away, okay?

Johnny spits out the ball-gag.

JOHNNY: I'll pay you twenty grand!

RALFI: You wouldn't believe the depths of shit you're—

Cut off as Johnny lashes out with one foot, kicking Ralfi in the balls, Yomomma going for Jane with the knife, Jane striking like a SNAKE, neatly severing the tendons in Yomomma's knife-wrist.

JANE: Fifty . . .

JOHNNY: *Done!*

Pretty jumps toward Jane, past Yomomma CLUTCHING her wrist in disbelief; she is met with a second kick to the head, goes down.

Jane whirls around, slices through Johnny's restraints.

Ralfi, bent double, clutching his crotch, edges toward the door . . .

Shinji poised to use the filament on Jane, but Johnny jumps off the table and heaves it at Shinji. The pistol falls to the ground.

The Yakuza guard bursts into the room. Jane instantly takes him out with a NINJA THROWING SPIKE square in the middle of his forehead. She has the second spike ready before Ralfi can get out. He smiles sickly.

Johnny dives for the pistol, jumps up, holds it on Shinji, backs up, moves Ralfi over next to Shinji with a gesture of the gun.

Shinji and Ralfi freeze, but Jane jumps on Yomomma, who was ready to get Johnny in the back, and starts whaling away.

JOHNNY: It's okay, I got the gun.

Jane keeps going, a staggering combination of blows.

JOHNNY: Enough!!!

Jane finally snaps to and realizes what she's doing. She gets off Yomomma, who is at least unconscious.

JOHNNY: Time to go.

They back toward the door. Slip through. Just as Johnny follows Jane, Shinji whips his filament. A moment too late. Because Ralfi was just stepping forward to take up the chase, it sings right past Ralfi's face.

RALFI: *You coulda fucking killed me!*

BEAT.

The filament whips through the air, once, twice. Ralfi falls to the floor in three neat pieces.

EXT. DROME BAR. STREET. NIGHT.

Johnny breaks from the door, desperate, not sure which way to run. Jane appears, grabs his arm, steering him down a narrow, trash-littered ALLEY.

HIGH POV watching from fire escape.

Jane starts clawing through the contents of a trash pile. Johnny looks back nervously.

JOHNNY: What the fuck are you *doing?*!

Jane pulls a battered shoulder bag from the pile. Shoves Johnny ahead of her.

JANE: *Move!!*

EXT. ALLEY. NIGHT.

Johnny stumbles against large poster, "NERVE ATTENUATION SYNDROME: IT'S NOT YOUR PROBLEM—YET," with big-eyed NAS poster-child.

JANE: *Run!!!*

Here comes Pretty. Shinji appears behind Pretty, aims past her, fires a BURST.

PUFFS of shredded paper on the head of the child in the NAS poster, where Shinji's shots land.

Johnny turns, aims the pistol, CLICK. Disgusted, he tosses the pistol away and runs. Jane, clutching her bag, on his heels.

Shinji tries to aim again, but Pretty is in the way.

EXT. STREETS. NIGHT.

Jane has taken the lead. Just before they round a corner, Johnny looks back. Pretty is gaining. They run into a maze of alleys.

Over garbage, past Dumpsters, the chase continues.

EXT. ALLEYS. NIGHT.

Jane pulls into another alley that has been built up into a sort of camp.

Assorted HOMELESS are here, in bedrolls and cardboard shacks; some with NAS. Jane leads Johnny deeper into the "camp."

SHINJI.

Following, looking pissed, deadly. He figures he's got them cornered now. Pretty with him.

EXT. ALLEYS. NIGHT.

Space with STACKED BUILDING MATERIALS, etc. Dark. Jane grabs Johnny, clasps her hand over his mouth.

JOHNNY   (*whispers*): I've gotta get *out* of here . . .

JANE   (*winded*): No. Stand. I'll take 'em.

BOOM of metal as Shinji jumps a gap. BOOM. Pretty follows. Jane produces more of her throwing spikes and pulls Johnny into shadow.

SHINJI.

He has his gun ready. Something RUSTLES. Shinji tracks the sound. Moves in. Listens.

BEAT. Someone WHISTLES. Someone else LAUGHS. A light comes on: an old storm lantern. A dozen pairs of EYES regard

Shinji from low angle: it's a group of LOTEK KIDS, *hunkered down around food they've scrounged up. They blink like owls, show no fear of Shinji and Pretty.*

But they're in their way. Shinji SMILES, makes a show of COCKING the gun and aiming it at one of them. BEAT.

AS ONE, the Lotek kids draw their WEAPONS. Some only have knives, but others have a variety of SPRING-DRIVE PRO-JECTILE WEAPONS. Their expressions haven't changed. They aren't about to move. The kid in Shinji's sights slowly cracks a tough urchin grin.

BEAT, as Shinji gets the picture: He can shoot one or two, but the others will get him. The RED DOT of a laser sight appears on Shinji's white shirt. Pretty backing off.

J-Bone steps from the shadows, his air bow in his arms.

Shinji smiles sickly, turns his head to notice a NUMBER OF HIS YAKUZA *arriving. Pretty is gone. The red dot remains on his shirt. It's a standoff. Shinji backs up slowly to the protection of his men.*

SHINJI: We'll find you again, Mr. Smith. Count on it . . .

Johnny and Jane watching from the carton maze as the Yakuza close rank around Shinji. The Lotek kids WHISTLE and JEER. J-Bone walks up to Johnny.

J-BONE: Said we were even. Now you owe me one.

He nods at them to follow him. A couple of LOTEK KIDS *ap-proach Jane. One GRINNING LOTEK KID, near Jane, points at her breasts.*

LOTEK KID: When'd you grow those, Janey?

HOWLS as she grabs finger, forcing him to his knees, dislocating his finger. J-Bone raises his brows.

J-Bone: Temper, sister.

Jane: Temper my ass, J-Bone.

J-Bone smiles. He leads them to a corner, pushes a large slab of plywood to one side, exposing a hidden exit.

J-Bone: Our back door . . .

Johnny and Jane pass through the opening. J-Bone turns to two of his Loteks.

J-Bone: Follow them . . .

EXT. STREETS. NIGHT.

Johnny and Jane come running down the street.

A Yakuza limo rounds the corner in the distance, tires SQUEALING.

Johnny: Shit.

Jane takes a few steps toward a manhole and heaves up the fifty-pound COVER. She SHOUTS over the CLANG as it hits the pavement.

Jane: Down!

Johnny scrambles down; she follows. The tires of the limo hiss past, a few feet away. BEAT. The feet of the two Loteks approach the manhole.

EXT. CHURCH OF THE RETRANSFIGURATION. NIGHT.

STREET PREACHER's VOICE BOOMS dim and hollow from the church as we TILT DOWN from sign to Yakuza LIMO pulling up.

Street Preacher   (*VO*): Some teach that these are the Final Days.

Others lose Faith utterly, brothers and sisters, but let *us* not be numbered among them . . .

DRIVER getting out with VID-PHONE and CRYO-UNIT, entering church.

STREET PREACHER (*cont'd*): . . . We have seen a new way, a new light. In this plague time, our goal is the vision of the Retransfiguration.

INT. CHURCH OF THE RETRANSFIGURATION. NIGHT.

A ragged SEA OF CANDLES. The Street Preacher, clad in a burgundy robe, clutching an ornate INVERTED CRUCIFIX, is in full rant to his congregation.

STREET PREACHER: To go forward, unflinching into the crucible of His technology—

CHORUS of amens. He lets his robe fall open as he raises his arm; we see many scars of implant surgery.

STREET PREACHER: I stand before you naked in the house of God, whole and strong! I, who was as you are! And I was made . . . *posthuman.*

The word "posthuman" sends a special shiver through the CROWD.

CLOSE ON Street Preacher as he notices the Yakuza driver entering the church.

STREET PREACHER: I sense a need for meditation, brothers and sisters . . . Leave me now . . . The sermon is ended.

Street Preacher turns to the altar, kneels dramatically in prayer. Congregation shuffles from chapel. Driver carefully places cryo-unit and vid-phone on floor, bows to Street Preacher, exits. Takahashi appears on the small screen.

TAKAHASHI (*VO, filter*): Good evening, Karl . . . I require your services. Again.

STREET PREACHER: We hold services nightly . . . You should join us.

TAKAHASHI (*VO, filter*): Your *talent*, I should say . . .

Street Preacher rises, turning to face vid-phone.

STREET PREACHER: You wish someone . . . *brought to Jesus?*

Street Preacher smoothly flips his crucifix, revealing the WICKED BLADE that protrudes from Christ's head, and shows it to the vid-phone.

STREET PREACHER: . . . Or brought to you?

TAKAHASHI (*VO, filter*): To me . . . But not entirely.

Street Preacher frowns. Takahashi explains.

TAKAHASHI (*VO, filter*): His head. Intact. The brain undamaged. Preserved in a cryo-unit.

STREET PREACHER: And who is this *lost soul* . . . this *sinner unrepentant?*

TAKAHASHI (*VO, filter*): A mnemonic courier. Not local. Name of "Johnny." Last seen at a club called the Drome . . .

Street Preacher frowns.

STREET PREACHER (*with grim satisfaction*): The very pit of Satan.

TAKAHASHI (*VO, filter*): Triple your usual fee if you deliver his head within twenty-four hours.

STREET PREACHER: Join me in the chapel, Mr. Takahashi. *Pray
with me* . . .

INT. YAKUZA LIMO. NIGHT.

Takahashi looking at vid-phone image of Street Preacher.

TAKAHASHI: *Do not fail me, Karl.*

The screen goes blank.

INT. ABANDONED SUBWAY. NIGHT.

Jane has pulled a flashlight from her bag. Lights the way.

JOHNNY: I have to get on-line . . . must be somebody I can talk to,
square this—

JANE: Fifty thou. You said. Time I see the color, right?

JOHNNY: Right. You were *terrific.* So if you'll just point the way out
and give me an account number for the cash transfer—

JANE: I'm on you till you *pay,* mister, no mistake.

BEAT.

JANE   (*cont'd*): How come they wanna cut off your head, anyway?
I mean, usually they just kill people, around here.

JOHNNY: Long story.

JANE: I'm not going anywhere till I get paid.

JOHNNY: I can carry nearly eighty gigs of data in my head, one-
sixty if I use a doubler. Trouble is, somebody's stuck in a lot
more than that and I don't know how to get it back out.

JANE: You're a smuggler.

FLASH FRAME. Johnny stumbles, wincing, clutching his head. Almost doubled over with pain.

JANE: Hey! What's wrong!?

After a moment, he performs the same meditative exercise we saw in the hotel bathroom. Gets control over the pain. He turns back to Jane.

JOHNNY: Junkie in Bangkok taught me that. Used to be a holy man . . .

He starts walking.

JANE: You from round there?

Johnny's not interested in conversation. FLASH FRAME. The pain comes back. Even worse. He stumbles against the wall, goes down on his knees . . .

JANE: Come on . . . over here . . .

She gets him up, leads over to a ledge.

JOHNNY: No . . . I've gotta keep . . .

JANE: Man . . . You are fucked up *severe* . . .

Checking his pupils with her light.

Something SPLASHES in the dark, behind them. Jane snaps her light off.

JANE: Stay put, okay?

She doubles back, moving silently, leaving him alone in the dark. He sinks back on the ledge and cradles his head in his hands.

INT. TAKAHASHI'S OFFICE. NIGHT.

Takahashi at his desk, a 3-D vid-sketch of Anna's face on his monitor.

TAKAHASHI   (*to himself*): I've seen you, I know . . . Before . . .

He punches commands; faces flip from the image bank, overlaying Anna's, looking for a match.

Takahashi watches for a moment, then gets up, goes to a cabinet in the corner, opens the door, which has a mirror on the inside. He takes a clean white shirt from a neat stack on a shelf and removes the one he is wearing, revealing his powerful, beautifully tattooed body.

As Takahashi puts on the fresh shirt, he HEARS something we don't. He reaches inside the cabinet, removes and unsheathes an antique samurai sword.

The door opens. Shinji enters with two of his MEN, an American and a Latino. Anxious secretary behind them.

SECRETARY: You can't just walk . . .

Takahashi nods to her. It's all right. Shinji gives an insolent bow. His henchmen explore the office. Takahashi fumes at them.

TAKAHASHI   (*in Japanese*): Who are these men?

SHINJI: They are my Kobuns.

Takahashi moves like lightning. He kills the American with a single, expert, lightning stroke. He kills the Latino, who had started to draw his gun, with two strokes. Very fast, but with

*great elegance and control. Sword in hand, Takahashi faces
Shinji across the fallen bodies.*

TAKAHASHI: I gave you no permission to have Kobuns.

*The dead Latino lies on his back. Takahashi rips the front of the
man's bloody shirt open and uses it to wipe his blade. We see
that the Latino is also heavily tattooed, the tatoos curving
around his back, over his shoulders and partially across his
chest.*

*Takahashi scrutinizes the tattoos without comment. Takahashi
points his sword at one of the designs.*

TAKAHASHI   (*in Japanese*): What does this mean?

*Shinji looks from the tattoo to Takahashi, then, very deliber-
ately, answers in English.*

SHINJI: It's Japanese . . .

BEAT.

TAKAHASHI: It is misspelled.

Shinji's eyes are on the sword.

TAKAHASHI   (*in Japanese, looking down at the bodies*): They are
honored to have been dispatched with such a fine instrument . . . (*looks at Shinji*) Twice you have attempted to capture
the courier in my territory. Twice you have failed. In neither
instance was I informed. That must not happen again.

Shinji is fuming at the insult.

SHINJI   (*in Japanese*): Yes, sir.

TAKAHASHI: Locate him. Inform me. I will supervise his capture. Understood?

SHINJI: Yes, sir.

TAKAHASHI: I want his head before morning. Is that clear?

Shinji bows, leaves. Takahashi steps around bodies, looks at the monitor on his desk.

ON THE MONITOR.

Still searching through the parade of faces . . .

INT. VILLA. STUDY. DAY.

Grainy, faded home movie quality. Inside a luxurious but cold study, a few child's toys are scattered. A WOMAN is at work behind the desk, her head bent over, so we can't see her face. The lighting is behind her, turning her into an ominous presence. A CHILD's POV hesitantly approaches the woman . . . As it moves in, the image bleaches, glitches . . . We hear a GASP . . .

CUT TO:

INT. UNDERGROUND TUNNEL. NIGHT.

Johnny wakes up with a start. His nose is bleeding again, but he doesn't notice. He sees Jane looking down on him, concerned. She's been standing guard. It takes him a moment to get his bearings, the dream has disturbed him. Then he realizes.

JOHNNY: You let me sleep!?

His anger takes her by surprise. She involuntarily takes a step back, knocking over her bag. STUFF tumbles out; weird mixture of weaponry and poor gaudy teen-girl junk. Makeup, gum wrappers, crumpled money, throwing spikes, sunglasses, credit cards. A HAND GRENADE on a key chain with a MINIA-TURE TROLL and a BEER OPENER . . . She grabs it.

JOHNNY: What's that?

Jane quickly puts the stuff back into her bag.

JANE: It's a *beer opener.*

She recovers her poise. Johnny returns to the issue at hand.

JOHNNY: I *told* you, I'm in a hurry . . . I'm a dead man, don't get this out of my head . . .

He hoists himself up. He becomes aware of his bloody nose, wipes it off. As he does so, he notices HIS HAND is oddly folded, two of the fingers are curled inward. He unfolds them, but when he lets go they curl inwards again. He hides his hand from Jane, but she's seen it. He starts walking. Jane tries to make conversation.

JANE: You ever sneak a look at what you're carrying?

JOHNNY: Usually there's a code, like a lock.

JANE: When there isn't?

JOHNNY: No. Goes with the territory. Safer for me, safer for the client . . . How come you knew those, uh . . .

JANE: Loteks, call 'em. I sort of hung with them. Before. How they fit that stuff in your head, anyway?

Johnny points to the small jack behind his ear.

JOHNNY: Implant. Wet-wired. I had to dump a lot of long-term memory.

JANE: Dump?

JOHNNY: My childhood.

Jane absorbs this. Incredulous. A little shocked.

JANE: All of it? You can't remember any of it?

JOHNNY: Maybe some residual stuff. Every now and then, there's something . . . I can never hold on to it . . .

BEAT.

JANE: That's seriously weird.

JOHNNY: Maybe I didn't lose anything I wanted to keep. I needed the space for the job.

JANE: You got parents 'n' stuff?

That weird glitch again, inside Johnny.

JOHNNY: *You* got parents?

JANE: Sure . . . One. Haven't seen him in years.

Johnny looks at her. Then he shrugs.

JOHNNY: Yeah . . . Anyway, I don't think about it.

JANE: So what do you think about? When you're alone?

The question hits a sensitive spot; Johnny deflects it.

JOHNNY: Right now I'm thinking about where we can go to log on the net.

Johnny speeds up his pace. No more talk.

INT. DROME BAR. BACK ROOM. NIGHT.

Hooky, with mop and pail, is cleaning the floor; quite a job, after Ralfi's demise, but he's almost done. Looks up as someone opens the door: Street Preacher, with the cyro-unit in one hand.

STREET PREACHER (*looking around*): The priest and the prophet have erred through strong drink. They err in vision, they stumble in judgment.

Crosses to table and puts cryo-unit on it.

STREET PREACHER: For all tables are full of vomit and filthiness, so that there is no place clean . . .

HOOKY: Shoulda seen it before.

STREET PREACHER: Isaiah.

HOOKY: Mine's Hooky.

STREET PREACHER (*snagging Hooky's earring*): Are you . . . saved, Hooky?

BEAT.

HOOKY: Not so's you'd notice . . .

Street Preacher leads Hooky to table, pops the door of the cyro-unit. Intense BLUE-WHITE LIGHT and a frosty puff of supercooled air. Takes Hooky's elbow and guides his prosthesis into the unit. BEAT. Withdraws it, WHITE with frost. Closes the unit. Hooky stares mournfully at his frozen hook.

STREET PREACHER: The girl. She took Ralfi's boy out of the back room. Who is she?

HOOKY: Mister, you think I can keep track of half the shit goes down in here?

Street Preacher picks up a heavy metal ashtray and smashes it down on Hooky's hook, which SHATTERS.

HOOKY: Man, why'd you have to do that?

Street Preacher conjures up the Jesus bowie and brings it down on his ear, ready to slice.

STREET PREACHER: *Who's the girl?*

Hooky folds.

HOOKY: Some wannabe. In here hustling for work.

STREET PREACHER: Name?

HOOKY: Jane.

STREET PREACHER: More.

HOOKY: One of Spider's jobs.

STREET PREACHER: Spider?

HOOKY: Flesh mechanic. Implants 'n' shit. They say he was like a legit doctor, before, had a license and everything . . .

STREET PREACHER: Where?

Hooky hesitates; Street Preacher puts a little pressure on the knife.

CUT TO:

EXT. HIGH ABOVE STREET. NIGHT.

Street Preacher exits the Drome Bar. Two Loteks, STUMP and TIBBS, are watching through binoculars with a tiny VIDEO CAMERA strapped above each lens.

STUMP: Whoa, Street Preacher's out. J-Bone, you copying?

INT. HEAVEN. NIGHT.

J-Bone sits on Victorian chair, watching vid-screen, which is optically combined with the Loteks' binoculars. TWO YOUNG LOTEKS are with him.

J-BONE: Look at that son of a bitch. Doesn't have a natural bone left in his body. So jacked up he oughta squeal when he walks. Takes that collection plate money and has himself shot up with Brazilian fetal tissue . . .

YOUNG LOTEK #1:   He really a preacher, J-Bone?

J-BONE: Motherfucker's got God and technology ass-backwards. Kills people for money to keep that steeple over his head.

STUMP   (*VO, filter*): Want us to follow him?

J-BONE: Keep the fuck away from him. Man's just too crazy . . .

INT. COMPUTER SHOP. NIGHT.

Blackness.

JANE   (*VO*): Slick. Where'd you learn to do that?

JOHNNY   (*VO*): Had this summer job . . .

WEDGE OF FAINT LIGHT as REAR DOOR opens. We can just make out Johnny, twisting a last connection into wires of open circuit box, the store's alarm system, as Jane steps through.

JANE: Doing what?

He follows.

JOHNNY: Breaking and entering.

INT. COMPUTER SHOP. BACK ROOM.

Shelves jammed with boxes. A desk littered with papers, etc. Johnny turns on desk lamp, sweeps everything else to the floor.

JOHNNY: Find me a Sino-Logic 16 . . .

Jane scans the shelves, pulls down a carton, passes it to him. He recites a list of the things he needs.

JOHNNY: Thomson eyephones . . . Sogo Seven data-gloves . . . GPL stealth module . . . one Burdine intelligent translator . . .

DISSOLVE TO:

LATER.

The Sino-Logic 16 looks like a super-fast laptop. It's connected, via a modem line, to the shop's phone. Johnny's connected all the various units. Turns on the computer.

Puts on goggles and gloves. Goggles leave his POV in DARK-NESS.

JOHNNY's POV as the goggles activate, sucking him into a RUSH through VIRTUAL REALITY. Rush STOPS. This version of cyberspace is a 3-D grid, densely arrayed with various SHAPES. Each shape represents data in a particular computer.

Our VR experience is always from JOHNNY's POV, as his "hands," simplified icons generated by the gloves, pick up and manipulate SHAPES. The shapes have a peculiar characteristic: when he opens one, it unfolds INFINITELY, surrounding his POV in that particular universe of data. He's doing it now, his "hands" quick and assured, BOXES WITHIN BOXES . . .

JANE's POV.

Johnny is sitting there, adroitly manipulating NONEXISTENT OBJECTS with his gloved hands, as serious about it as if he were disarming a bomb. It looks goofy, ABSURD.

JANE   (*VO*): What're you doing?

JOHNNY: Making a long-distance call . . . Beijing . . . A hotel . . .

JOHNNY's POV.

As something ADMITS him. The BEIJING HOTEL TRADEMARK glows for an instant, red neon. A VIRTUAL SCREEN appears, scrolling DATA. We follow Johnny's moves as he fishes for a particular fragment of information.

JOHNNY   (*VO*): Fax charges for Suite 2571 . . . 15 January, 2021 . . . say 11:15 PM, 11:30 . . .

Data in tighter RESOLUTION. It's in CHINESE alphanumerics.

JOHNNY   (*VO*): On-line translation . . .

Chinese becomes ENGLISH.

JOHNNY   (*VO*): Shit.

JANE's POV.

He "looks" up at her, eyes covered by the massive goggles.

JOHNNY: It's just an all-night copy shop. They were sending the fax to a copy shop. Here. In Newark.

She doesn't know what he's talking about. His hands start to move again, very fast.

His POV. His hands untangling a knot of data. Another VIR-TUAL SCREEN leaps out of it. Hand icons moves to another box . . .

INT. YAKUZA COMPUTER CENTRAL. NIGHT.

SAME POV.

Of the hand and the box. Then the picture ZOOMS out and turns into a grid, a HIGH-REZ MAP of Newark. An ARROW pulsing at one spot.

A YAKUZA OPERATOR removes his goggles, speaks into his head set.

MAN #1:   Got him. 5326 Sutton Plaza, Sub Level 3.

EXT. NEWARK STREET. NIGHT.

A Yakuza limo hangs a U-turn, speeds into the night . . .

INT. COMPUTER SHOP. NIGHT.

JOHNNY's POV.

As another VIRTUAL SCREEN blips out of another box.

JOHNNY: Hold it, *hold* it . . . c'mon, baby, all the way . . . Back to
            Newark . . . Copy shop . . . Yeah, it's *here*! Part of it's here, in
            the buffer of their fax modem . . .

JANE's POV.

On Johnny's face. Hope and expectation become bitter disappointment in an instant.

JOHNNY's POV.

CU on virtual screen: "HOLD FOR DR. ALLCOME. WILL CALL."

JOHNNY: *Nothing.* Nothing but a name. "Dr. Allcome." Nothing came through . . . *Shit!*

Closes his gloved fist, TIGHT.

JOHNNY'S POV.

As we REVERSE, dizzingly, through the computer-animations that have constituted cyberspace, boxes refolding and jumping back into boxes . . .

JANE (*VO*): Let's go, okay?

JOHNNY (*VO*): No. I'm going to try something else. Guy called Strike . . .

We move through cyberspace again.

JOHNNY (*VO*): He runs a board in this sector. Owes me a favor. Maybe he can find this doctor for me—

We're there: STRIKE'S "board" is a smooth gray cube. Johnny goes to work on it.

JOHNNY (*VO*): Come *on*, man, let me *in* . . .

EXT. STREET. OUTSIDE COMPUTER SHOP. NIGHT.

The Yakuza limo hisses around the corner, approaches the computer shop . . .

INT. COMPUTER SHOP. BACK ROOM. NIGHT.

A WINDOW opens in the side of the cube: a virtual screen. Strike is on it, digitally disguised.

STRIKE: Get off my board, man! You're too hot! You're a hit waiting to happen! Off!

JOHNNY   (*VO*): You owe me, Strike . . .

STRIKE: Hey, I don't owe you *that* much!

JOHNNY   (*VO, bluffing*): I can crash you from here. You know I can. Wipe out your entire board . . .

STRIKE: Johnny, don't, man, that's my livelihood . . .

JOHNNY: I need to know what I'm holding, Strike. Why's the Yakuza after it? Who's Dr. Allcome?

STRIKE: All I know is you got a head full of Pharmakom data and the Yakuza want you *bad*!

JOHNNY: *Pharmakom?*

Strike CRINGES as a change shoots across his field of data, the texture twisting and coarsening. He looks at this with horror.

STRIKE: Shit! They put a virus on us! Get out of here, man! I never heard of any Dr. Malcom, I never—

He stops in horror as suddenly part of his image disappears. Then another part. Like someone working an eraser. Strike vanishes with a digital SCREAM as the VIRUS eats his image.

INT. COMPUTER SHOP. NIGHT.

Jane's restless, nervous as a cat but just as quiet. Slips through the shop to the display window.

JANE's POV.

Nothing moving out there.

She takes a MAKEUP MIRROR from her bag and extends it into the window, sideways, tilting it, using it like a periscope. CU MIRROR on various views of the street. Nothing.

Then she sees YAKUZA *approaching, keeping close to the shadows of the buildings: figures in LONG BLACK COATS.*

JANE: Shit . . .

Scrambles for the back room . . .

INT. COMPUTER SHOP. BACK ROOM. NIGHT.

JOHNNY's *POV on Strike's cube as something starts to MORPH out of it, something with a much higher bit rate, finer resolution. Anna, crazy delight in her eyes at seeing Johnny.*

JOHNNY   (*genuinely baffled*): Who the hell are *you?*

Anna's face crumples with SORROW; she's about to speak when . . .

Jane rips the goggles off, taking Anna and cyberspace with them.

JANE: Move! Move!

Sound of BREAKING GLASS.

CUT TO:

THE YAKUZA.

Kicking in the front door. Shinji behind his men . . .

INT. COMPUTER SHOP. NIGHT.

Jane reaches into her bag, comes out with the grenade key chain . . .

Johnny diverts to grab a brightly printed carton ("INFOBAHN 3000") from STOCK SHELF . . .

Jane pulls the pin and tosses the grenade toward the door. She frantically swerves to grab Johnny and pull him out.

INT. SERVICE ALLEY. NIGHT.

KA-BOOM!! Johnny and Jane CRASH out the service entrance and run, Johnny with carton under arm. The explosion shaking building behind them.

JOHNNY: A *beer* opener?!

Jane shrugs. They keep running.

EXT. COMPUTER SHOP. NIGHT.

Shinji gets up from where the explosion has thrown him. Dusts himself off. His men lie dead or wounded, MOANING. Shinji pays them no mind, his eyes burning with humiliation and fury.

INT. UNDERGROUND MALL AREA. NIGHT.

Seedy, ill-lit, nearly deserted. At counter, Jane picks up two coffees in paper cups and carries them over to Johnny.

Johnny taking the INFOBAHN 3000 from carton; it has numerical KEYPAD, a small SCREEN, but is unlike vid-phones we've seen. A short CURLY CORD ends in a CLIP for PHONECARDS.

JANE: Great. Now I'm a waitress.

Johnny's sorting through a thick deck of credit cards.

JOHNNY: I can't use any of these. The Yakuza's watching the net, waiting for the first transaction . . .

Jane sits down. Her bag is on the table. Johnny turns it over, dumping the contents on the table.

JANE: Hey!

He pulls a phone-card out of the pile.

JOHNNY: Mind if I use this?

Jane SIGHS. CLOSE on Johnny's hands as he slips her card into the Infobahn clip.

JANE: Man owes me fifty thou and he's scamming my phone-card.

JOHNNY *(grins)*: And it's still our first date . . .

Johnny gets up and heads for the pay vid-phone in the back.

INT. UNDERGROUND MALL. COFFEE SHOP. VID-PHONE. NIGHT.

Johnny slots clipped card in phone. Gets DIAL TONE.

JOHNNY: Number for Pharmakom Industries. Their branch here in Newark.

A number appears on the screen. He dials ON INFOBAHN. PHARMAKOM logo appears over gorgeous sunset clouds.

VOICE MAIL *(VO)*: You have reached the offices of Pharmakom Incorporated, a subsidiary of Pharmakombinat. If you know the number of the section—

JOHNNY: Head of security . . .

As he works Infobahn keypad like an ace. ON PAYPHONE SCREEN as pretty logo is replaced by PHARMAKOM INTER-

NATIONAL PHONEBOOK. As Johnny HACKS and we ZERO IN on the NUMBER. We hear it RING. Pharmakom SECURITY MAN appears on screen. Peers narrowly at Johnny.

SECURITY: This number is unlisted. It's a federal offense—

JOHNNY: Don't like surprises?

SECURITY: No. Not at all.

JOHNNY: I have 320 gigabytes of Pharmakom data.

This gets Security's FULL attention. He glances sideways as if making eye contact OS; shoulder movement suggests he is using keyboard OS.

JOHNNY: Don't bother. I'll be out of here in twenty seconds.

BEAT.

SECURITY: What do you want?

JOHNNY: Your data, out of my head. I've got one image, you have the other two . . .

BEAT.

SECURITY   (*lying*): That can be arranged . . .

JOHNNY: Let's meet.

SECURITY: Where?

INT. UNDERGROUND MALL. NIGHT.

Johnny walking fast, trying to outdistance her.

JANE: You're crazy! They'll chop your head off!

She's right, but Johnny has convinced himself.

JOHNNY: These guys will negotiate. They're corporate.

JANE: So's the Yakuza!

JOHNNY: Listen, if you don't come, fine. It's a business meeting. It's not your kind of scene. If it works out, I'll get you the money I owe you. If it doesn't—

JANE: If it doesn't, you're dead!

He rounds on her.

JOHNNY: *I'm gonna be dead anyway, I don't get this shit out of my head!*

Stung, she stops. He walks on. She takes a step. Something's affected her coordination.

JANE: H-hey! Listen! This guy Spider? Used to be a doctor? H-he could f-fix you, maybe, your head . . .

Johnny looks back, sees her condition.

JOHNNY: Hey. What's with you?

JANE: I'll . . . aaaaah . . . b-be all r-r-r—

Johnny grabs her as she starts to sink to the ground. In this instant, he's instinctively assumed responsibility—but with it, he panics; looking around as if he'll be able to hand her to someone else; here, you take care of her.

PASSERSBY *stare briefly, walk on as if they haven't seen.*

JOHNNY: Jesus! You're sick. You strung out or what?

Shakes her head; shudders, trying to pull herself together by sheer force of will. Johnny looks up, horrified as he realizes . . .

JOHNNY: You got NAS!

JANE: *No!!!*

Her eyes roll up. Johnny has to lift her in his arms.

JOHNNY: I've got a *meet!*

She manages to subdue it, long enough to speak, but . . .

JANE: G-go . . . G-g . . .

JOHNNY: I can't deal with this now, understand?

He carries her to a nearby doorway and puts her down.

JOHNNY: Whatever it is, you're sidelined, right? I gotta make this meeting—

Her eyes roll up.

JOHNNY: Hey! Can you hear me?

She snaps back into focus.

JANE: Spider. He's g-got d-drugs . . . He's got a p-place . . . Not too far from here . . .

Johnny looks down at her. At his watch. At her. He's at the end of his tether, at war with himself and furious he has been put in this position.

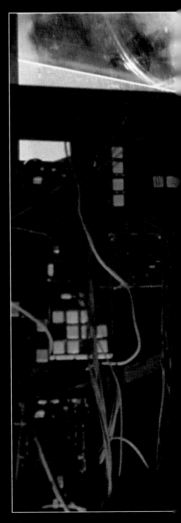

EXT. LANDFILL. IN FRONT OF SPIDER'S GARAGE. NIGHT.

A crazy facade of graffitied sheet metal. Johnny half drags, half carries Jane out of a cab. She can barely walk, her left leg making weird robotic movements.

Johnny props Jane against the wall beside a crudely installed intercom/videocam unit; presses the button, waits impatiently.

SPIDER   (*VO*): If you aren't expected you aren't invited. So fuck off, okay?

JOHNNY: Jane. She says you know her.

SPIDER   (*VO*): Janey?

JOHNNY: Get down here, man! She's sick!

He pushes Jane up to the intercom/videocam.

JANE: H-hey . . . Spider, babe . . . I . . .

Johnny tries to hold her upright as she starts to convulse. He can't. She's thrashing in a puddle. Blood at the corner of her mouth.

Door CRASHES open; Spider rushes out.

SPIDER: Get your wallet in her mouth!

Johnny whips out wallet; it flips open, spraying credit cards. He wedges it between her teeth. Spider picks her up in fireman's carry, while Johnny scrambles to pick up his cards.

He ducks in after Spider just before the door slams shut.

INT. SPIDER'S GARAGE. NIGHT.

One side is taken up by a strange looking VAN. PAN across a scary surgical table, sophisticated medical equipment and mechanic's gear—like a cross between an abortion clinic and a transmission shop.

Johnny helps Spider carry Jane to the surgical table. Spider is moving fast, Jane's condition has his total attention; it's critical. He slips a band of electrodes down over her forehead. He consults a monitor.

JOHNNY: Look, I gotta run—

SPIDER: Shut up. Give me the muscle relaxant. The red one!

Johnny finds a pistol-like plastic INJECTOR in a jumble of tools and instruments, passes it to Spider. Spider tugs at Jane's T-shirt, exposing skin; presses muzzle of injector against it, fires.

CU the muzzle coming away; dime-sized reddish mark. Jane SIGHS, stretches, her muscles unkinking.

JOHNNY: It's NAS, right?

SPIDER: Yeah, the black shakes. Like half the people walking around this town . . .

He looks at Johnny, his eyes narrowing with suspicion, jealousy.

SPIDER: Who are you? New boyfriend?

Johnny doesn't answer. Spider lays out probes and instruments. Suddenly he stops.

SPIDER: You just understand one thing, okay?

JOHNNY: What's that?

SPIDER: It wasn't *my* work got her this way. My work is *clean.* Besides, you don't get this shit from amp jobs. That's just a *myth.*

He's so intense we immediately doubt it.

JOHNNY: So what *does* cause it?

SPIDER: Cause it? The world causes it.

He starts grabbing things: computer screens, disk drives, light bulbs, a vid-phone . . .

SPIDER: This causes it . . . this causes it . . . this causes it . . . *(grabs Johnny)* You cause it . . . I cause it . . . Information *overload.* All the electronics around you, poisoning the airwaves. Technological fucking civilization! But we still have all this shit, 'cause *we can't live without it.* Now, let me do my work.

He picks up a sharp, ugly instrument. Johnny turns away, looks around the room. OS, nasty machine noises; Johnny glances in that direction, winces. Then he spots Spider's computer setup: a futuristic PC attached to fancy peripherals, covering a twenty-foot table. He's drawn to it like a moth to a flame. Picks up the telephone handset, glances to make sure Spider is busy, punches in a number. We hear it RING.

PHARMAKOM RECEPTIONIST: Pharmakom Incorporated . . .

But the DIAL TONE sounds again as the connection is broken, the screen saver comes back on and immediately starts to MORPH into the image of Anna. Johnny pulls back, spooked.

JOHNNY: . . . You . . . ? Who—

ANNA: Johnny—

JOHNNY: Huh. I'm losing it . . .

ANNA: Losing! Yes! We have both lost so much—

JOHNNY: I'm seeing things. Right? Seeing things . . .

ANNA: Yes, Johnny! Seeing things! But you must remember how it
    all felt! How each thing smelled and tasted! You used to like to
    put your tongue against the iron railing, and look out across
    the park. You told me it made a taste in your mouth like blood.
    Let me take you home, Johnny—

Johnny's reaction. Where does she get this from?

SPIDER   (*OS, angry*): What do you think you're doing!?

*Immediately, Anna dissolves back into the innocuous screen
saver. Johnny notices the handset BEEPING. Replaces it.*

JOHNNY: Just—just looking.

SPIDER: Don't touch *anything*. Who the fuck *are* you?

JOHNNY: Johnny.

SPIDER: Johnny who?

JOHNNY: Just Johnny . . .

*FLASH FRAME. He winces as his head gives him another jolt.
Spider looks at him, curious. Johnny scans the lab around
them.*

JOHNNY: Looks like a full-service shop . . . How are you on brain
    implants?

Spider sizes him up.

JOHNNY: Silicon implants. Neural overlays. Memory augmenta-
    tion.

Spider moves a little closer, sizing Johnny up.

SPIDER: Don't see that in Newark much. Just Johnny. Kinda up-scale for us, you know?

JOHNNY: Got mine in Singapore.

SPIDER: What's the deal, Just Johnny?

JOHNNY: I got this problem. Up here. Maybe you can help me.

CUT TO:

INT. SPIDER'S GARAGE. NIGHT.

Johnny in dentist's chair, Spider SCANNING HIS HEAD. Studying results on a monitor.

ON THE MONITOR.

The inside of Johnny's head. The implant itself is small. But throughout his brain, dark streaks, almost like oil, are blurring the neural pathways. Spider WHISTLES.

SPIDER: Man, they did some serious shoehorning to get that in . . .

JOHNNY: Let's skip the technical critique, okay? I need some *help* here.

SPIDER: You don't know the half of it. Must be hurting like hell.

JOHNNY: Think I need you to tell me that? I got *three hundred and twenty gigs* in there.

We see Spider react to the number. He is very interested now; he's being very careful.

SPIDER: Yeah? What is it, exactly? What kind of stuff?

BEAT.

JOHNNY   (*with care; lying*): Haven't got a clue . . . And I don't have a download code either.

EXT. SPIDER'S GARAGE. NIGHT.

Sound of boots on pavement. One of Johnny's credit cards still lies in the mud. Street Preacher's heavy boot stops beside it. Bends down. Picks up the credit card. Runs his fingers over it. He looks up, looking for a way in. Follows the wall, around the corner, out of sight.

CUT TO:

INT. SPIDER'S GARAGE. NIGHT.

Jane appears, drug-stunned but anxious, draped in a sheet. She sees Johnny in the chair.

JANE: You . . . doin' okay?

SPIDER   (*with a strange smile*): Good girl, Janey. You brought him to the right place.

JANE: You can fix him?

SPIDER: I don't know. (*calculating look at Johnny*) With this kind of seepage, if I can work a download, I'm not sure the product would be coherent.

JOHNNY: Fuck the product. I just want it *out*.

SPIDER: I wish it were that simple . . .

JOHNNY   (*impatient*): Allcome. Dr. Allcome. Ever hear that name?

Spider looks at Johnny, pretending to have misunderstood, but we can see that he has heard of Dr. Allcome.

SPIDER: Holcomb?

JOHNNY: Allcome. Like *All . . . come.*

BEAT. Spider shrugs.

SPIDER: Maybe . . .

Johnny jumps out of the chair.

JOHNNY: Where *is* he?

SPIDER: I said "maybe." Why do you want to see him?

JANE: C'mon, Spider!

He turns to Jane, oozing concern. Puts a protective arm around her. Like a father, but also a bit like a lover.

SPIDER: Don't worry. I'll make sure Just Johnny gets to see who he needs to see. But you, you need *bed rest*, Janey. Downtime. *Big time.*

Something in her wants to buy this; he's her surgeon, her mentor, they've slept together, she's barely recovered from her attack . . .

JANE: But . . . He's my *client* . . .

SPIDER: I'm tellin' you, you gotta sleep!

JOHNNY: Just *tell* me where to go!

BEAT. Spider glances at Jane. Her approval of him important.

SPIDER: I'll drive you.

He precedes them to the back door.

EXT. SPIDER'S GARAGE. NIGHT.

They step out and see an ancient STEP-UP VAN retrofitted with a huge, blimplike gasbag on top. A jumble of gas lines protrude from the gasbag and run around to the exhaust. A Spider logo on its side. Johnny stares.

SPIDER: Methane. Beats hell out of waiting on Esso.

EXT. SPIDER'S GARAGE. NIGHT.

Street Preacher circling the building, starting to RUN as he hears NOISY IGNITION and BACKFIRING of van.

INT. SPIDER'S VAN. NIGHT.

All in. Spider steps on the gas. Slowly . . .

As the van turns around the building, Street Preacher appears, rushing straight toward them, like a locomotive.

SPIDER: Fuck.

He FLOORS IT, heading straight for Street Preacher, who DIVES, AIMING for the windshield, STRIKES, shattering it, and ROLLS OFF, vanishing.

Tires SCREAM as Spider hangs an insanely tight turn and they ROAR up street, away from garage. Johnny looks at Spider.

JOHNNY: Who the fuck was *that*?!

BEAT. Spider cranes to see around crack-webbed impact point.

SPIDER: You don't want to know.

EXT. PAVEMENT BESIDE SPIDER'S GARAGE. NIGHT.

Street Preacher on hands and knees. Shakes himself. Getting to his feet, bloody but unbowed.

EXT. STREETS. NIGHT.

Spider's van races through the night.

INT. TAKAHASHI'S OFFICE. NIGHT.

Takahashi is at his desk, the image of Anna in front of him, matched with a more formal portrait. His secretary reads from another monitor.

SECRETARY: Anna Kalmann. Founder. Former CEO of the multinational Pharmakombinat Industrie, Zurich. Born, 1 August 1965. Died, 3 September 2015.

TAKAHASHI: Died? Six years ago?

SECRETARY: She was imprinted to Pharmakom's neural-net installation in Zurich prior to onset of morbidity.

TAKAHASHI: Imprinted?

SECRETARY: Her neural-net persona has Swiss citizenship, under the Artificial Intelligence Laws of 2006. She advises the current board from—

A LOTEK scrawl erases Anna's portrait; intense burst of ROCK, cut off as the secretary switches off the screen. But Takahashi has missed this, turning away.

TAKAHASHI: A ghost . . .

EXT. SIDE OF UNION STATION. NIGHT.

Spider's van swerves around a corner and pulls into a loading bay of the disused Art Deco station.

INT. UNION STATION. NIGHT.

Dark. Light angles in from elsewhere in the building as Spider opens a door, leading Johnny and Jane up the stairs . . .

INT. STATION HALL. NIGHT.

They emerge into a huge hall filled with NAS PATIENTS *in advanced stages of the disease.* ORDERLIES *put bodies on stretchers,* NURSES *tend to their patients, everything is make-shift.*

There are far too many patients, far too few personnel.

Johnny and Jane stare in horror; Spider doesn't even seem to notice. He gestures to them and they follow him as he finds a path through the room. He takes a white coat from a rack, slips it on as he goes.

A NURSE, *who seems to be an NAS patient herself, looks up.*

NURSE: Spider, thank God you're here . . .

Spider goes over to her and helps check out her PATIENT. *They talk together. Spider nods briefly.*

SPIDER: Come with me.

They move on toward a tentlike structure that partitions a corner of the hall. The nurse smiles at Johnny as he passes. Along the way, Spider stops at various patients, looks at them, checks charts, etc., making sure Johnny gets a good look at the suffering that goes on here.

JOHNNY: Where's Dr. Allcome?

SPIDER: "Dr. Allcome" is who we page in hospitals if we got a major problem and we don't want to spook the civilians.

JANE: Huh?

SPIDER: "Dr. Allcome to Ward Seven." And we all drop everything and haul ass to wherever. Usually it means we got a crazy, somebody violent . . . It means we need all the help we can get.

JOHNNY: But I saw it on a fax buffer—

They have reached the tentlike partition and Spider precedes Johnny and Jane inside.

INT. TENT/OPERATING ROOM. NIGHT.

Jury-rigged by someone who is endlessly inventive. Some genuine medical equipment is mixed freely with homemade contraptions and gadgets. Spider, Johnny and Jane enter. Spider directs Johnny to an operating table.

SPIDER: That fax was supposed to be for us.

BEAT, as Johnny digests this. Still suspicious.

JOHNNY: Who's "us"?

SPIDER: The NAS underground. People who keep this place going. People like me. Get on the table here.

JOHNNY: Why?

SPIDER: Don't be a bigger asshole than you have to, okay? Lie down.

Johnny obeys. Spider pushes something that looks like a modern version of a CAT scanner in place.

SPIDER: Now let's take a better look at that shit . . .

He throws a series of switches, a WHIRRING sound. Images and numbers display on a console. Spider nods, as if his suspicions have been confirmed.

SPIDER: No access code?

JOHNNY: Except for one image. Out of three.

He reaches for his pocket, but Spider shakes his head.

SPIDER: It won't help. What did they use, random images?

JOHNNY: From the TV.

Spider nods. He's not hopeful.

SPIDER: Okay, I've got some decryption programs here. We'll run them, see if we get anything.

He pops in a few discs, the WHIRRING sounds again. The program runs. Spider sits back, looks over to Jane, who's staring at Johnny.

SPIDER: Janey, honey, you should really lie down.

JANE: Can you break the code, Spider?

SPIDER: If I get lucky. *Really* lucky.

Jane's eyes return to Johnny. Concern. Spider notices the way she looks at him. We can see it bothers him. The WHIRRING stops. Spider CURSES softly.

JOHNNY: No dice?

Spider pushes away the CAT-scan gear.

SPIDER: No. But I can get it out.

JOHNNY: How?

SPIDER: With a general anesthetic, a cranial drill, and pair of forceps.

BEAT.

JOHNNY: You're *joking*, right?

SPIDER: No joke.

JOHNNY: And I could die, too, right?

SPIDER: It's going to kill you anyway, when it ruptures. I take it out, you'll probably survive. You'd lose some fine-motor skills, you might not be able to remember anything for more than about three minutes, but—

JOHNNY: Fuck that.

Spider comes closer to Johnny.

SPIDER: Let me tell you something. Let's start with what you got inside there. Just so you know what it's worth, okay? What it's worth to the world. (*BEAT*) You're carrying the cure to NAS.

Johnny studies him carefully; is this bullshit? Can't decide.

JOHNNY: You're telling me I got—

SPIDER: Pharmakom's complete R&D on their cure for Nerve Attenuation Syndrome, plus the records of the field trials to prove it works. And it *works like a motherfucker.*

JANE: Like a *real* cure?

SPIDER: They could have you straightened out in three weeks, Janey. You and everybody else.

Johnny has hit upon an inconsistency in Spider's story.

JOHNNY: Everybody's trying to cut *off* my fucking head—

SPIDER: So they can take it back to Saigon and run it under a quantum interference detector. But then they'd have the cure, and we wouldn't. You leave that thing in your head, nobody can save you. Plus the cure is lost. Forever. Let me take it out, I can save the cure. Even if we had the code, the seepage is so bad, it would probably come out as garbage . . .

JOHNNY: What's it supposed to matter to me? If I'm dead. You follow me?

SPIDER: The cure can save millions of lives. You're gonna die anyway if we don't get it out. You can make a difference.

Johnny is not sure what to believe.

JOHNNY: All I know is that whatever's in my head is worth a lot of money. Why should I trust you? (*turns to Jane*) You're supposed to be my bodyguard here.

Jane stands, looking back and forth from one to the other: what the hell are the alternatives here, anyway?

A rolling stretcher CRASHES through the tent flap, flies across the room and SMASHES into the wall. The nurse's body falls from the stretcher: eyes dead, her neck broken.

Street Preacher enters, hands spread as if about to launch into a sermon, his face aglow with the possibilities of what he's just heard.

STREET PREACHER: Praise be unto the Lord. That cure is *mine*...
    Behold your Savior!

Spider makes an instant decision.

SPIDER: Run for it!

*He hurls himself at Street Preacher, who plucks him out of the
air and tosses him aside. Advances on Johnny.*

*Johnny, next to the operating table, grabs a SCALPEL and
hurls it at Street Preacher, who deflects it easily. Jane lets loose
with TWO quick THROWING SPIKES in a row. Street Preacher
plucks one out of the air, but the other plants itself in his
shoulder. Street Preacher GRUNTS, then plucks the spike
from his shoulder. Pissed off at his own sloppiness.*

*Spider tackles Street Preacher around the legs, bringing him
down.*

SPIDER: *Run!!* Get to Jones! Maybe he can do it!

*Jane and Johnny stand for a brief moment, unwilling to accept
Spider's sacrifice.*

SPIDER: *Jones,* Janey!! Get him to *Jones!!*

*Street Preacher lifts Spider and HURLS him against the wall.
Spider on the floor. Not moving.*

*Johnny grabs Jane, pulls her away. They finally run for it. Jane
looking back over her shoulder to Spider. Street Preacher gets
up, looks after them, is about to follow when a movement from
Spider catches his eye. He approaches Spider, hoists him up.*

INT. UNION STATION. NIGHT.

Johnny and Jane RUN into a tunnel...

INT. TENT/OPERATING ROOM. NIGHT.

Street Preacher holds Spider against the wall.

STREET PREACHER: Who is Jones?

SPIDER: Deals hot wetware in Cleveland . . .

STREET PREACHER: You can't lie to me, sinner. *Jesus is my co-pilot . . .*

Reaching for Spider, who makes a very good try at kicking Street Preacher in the balls and diving past him, but it doesn't work. Caught in those big hands, Spider's flung back against the wall. Street Preacher's eyes fall on the surgical tools. He stares reverently. Then turns his attention back to Spider.

STREET PREACHER: Tell me where they *are . . .*

Street Preacher drives a scalpel through the open palm of Spider's left hand, through the plywood, pinning him there.

INT. MAINTENANCE TUNNEL. NIGHT.

Johnny and Jane hurry along; Jane keeps looking back. A SCREAM echoes eerily. Johnny and Jane stop, spooked, knowing Spider is gone. Johnny touches Jane on the shoulder. It's a tender, protective gesture. They continue.

EXT. DARK STREETS. NIGHT.

Spider's van races through the night.

INT. SPIDER'S VAN. NIGHT.

ON SCREEN of funky dashboard VID-PHONE as PHAR-MAKOM SECURITY MAN appears. Johnny, driving one-handed, adjusts the dash-phone's camera so Security can only see him, not Jane next to him. We notice the Infobahn 3000 plugged into the dash-phone.

JOHNNY: I couldn't make the meet, but I'm still up for it. Are you?

SECURITY: Certainly.

JOHNNY: This time the place is Heaven. Under the bridge in Landfill 5 . . . Bring the rest of the code.

SECURITY: I'll be there.

Johnny breaks the connection. Jane looks at him.

JANE: Great. Now if he doesn't kill you, J-Bone will . . .

Johnny shrugs. Speeds on.

INT. TAKAHASHI'S OFFICE. NIGHT.

ON A MONITOR on Takahashi's desk. On it, the Pharmakom security man slumps, eyes blank, mouth open, as if brain-dead.

PULL BACK to Takahashi with his hand in a VIDEO PUPPET GLOVE connected to the monitor. He wiggles his fingers. On the monitor, the security man's eyes and tongue pop out, squirm grotesquely.

TAKAHASHI: He wants the code . . .

Making the puppet image speak in SYNC. There is no security man. Takahashi removes his hand from the glove, but the video puppet on the screen doesn't go limp. It turns and SMILES at him, MORPHS into Anna.

ANNA: Listen to me, Takahashi, before it's too late . . .

Takahashi's eyes bug with a mixture of rage and occult Rashomon terror. Deep down, he believes in ghosts.

ANNA: Your daughter is gone and you feel that as a great wrong. But I offer you the chance to right a greater wrong—

TAKAHASHI   (*exaggerated calm*): No. This is not happening.

He reaches to shut off the monitor, but something in her look stops him.

ANNA: I've learned so many things since my death, Takahashi. I fled into the net, and I saw everything, I saw that they had—

CLICK. He shuts off the monitor. Stares at the blank screen, breathing deeply.

EXT. RATLANDS. NIGHT.

The rubble-strewn plain, the BRIDGE in BACKGROUND.

Johnny and Jane pull up below bridge in Spider's van.

EXT. HEAVEN. LOOKOUT. NIGHT.

VARIOUS ANGLES establishing Heaven. Its bulging patch-work flank suggests the world's largest tree house, built by several generations of hardcore Wild Boys.

We MOVE IN—as if approaching a spaceship made of garbage. Here's the VW-BOMBER, a device designed to hold and drop three VOLKSWAGEN BUGS. The VWs are STACKED like bombs; through their shattered windows, we see hundreds of GLASS jars and jugs of an amber fluid—GASOLINE.

We TILT DOWN this mad contraption to a small PLATFORM, where STICK, a young Lotek, and his BUDDY are on sentry duty, shooting the shit, apparently stoned.

STICK: So I told her, if she wants to get with me, I want to get with
    her and screw the physical disabilities, it's all about feeling,
    right . . . ?

Buddy holds up his hand, cocks his head.

STICK: What?

BUDDY: Wind, maybe . . .

EXT. BELOW BRIDGE. NIGHT.

Johnny sounds van's HORN, leaning in through the window,
YELLING hoarsely

JOHNNY: Hey! Wake up, dammit! Hey . . . ! Listen up!!

No sign of life from above. Johnny stops, discouraged. He's
unusually quiet, something preying on his mind.

JOHNNY: Hey . . . Did you . . . What do you think? I mean it's crazy,
    but if that's really the cure for NAS in my head, it could save
    you . . . it could save everybody . . .

She looks at him, trying to figure out what he's getting at.

JANE: So?

JOHNNY: I don't know! Who's this Jones guy Spider said was our
    only chance? . . .

He starts rummaging through the junk, trying to hide his
awkwardness.

JANE: He's . . . uh, it's . . . He was in the Navy. In the War. They put a
    lot of stuff in his head. Like you, sort of—

*Gets his full attention. He's picked up a battered trash-can lid
and a stick.*

JOHNNY: Memory augments?

JANE: I'm not sure. Anyway, he's . . . (*shrugs, at a loss*) You'll see . . .

*BEAT. Johnny senses she's holding something back. Then he
glances up to Heaven and starts banging the stick on the trash-
can lid, a loud RACKET.*

EXT. HEAVEN. PLATFORM. NIGHT.

Stick cranes out over black void, listening.

STICK: Somebody *crazy*, down there . . . Getting on my nerves . . .

BUDDY: Ratland's fulla crazies, Stick. Ignore, man.

STICK: Hey, look. It's Spider's van . . . Let's drop a bug on the Spider, man . . .

Stick's only kidding, to bug Buddy.

BUDDY: Hey, don't even say that! J-Bone'll *shit*, he hears you, you
know how jumpy he's been—

*Stick is only baiting Buddy; now he's climbing up to the LEVER
that releases the VWs.*

BUDDY: *Hey!* Shit, man—

Stick GRINS; enjoying putting Buddy uptight.

STICK: Hey nothin'. It's what they're for . . .

*Stick with his hand on the lever, just jacking Buddy up. Then
his FOOT SLIPS; look of horror as he's forced to grab the lever
to keep from falling. SWINGS DOWN on lever.*

BUDDY: Oh shit . . . !

Multi-stage action of BOMBER mechanism as bottom-most VW is released; it shoots down RAMP, still attached by RIP-CORD to INCENDIARY FUSE. Cord goes taut; fuse IGNITES.

EXT. BELOW BRIDGE. NIGHT.

Jane's oblivious as the falling VW catches fire. Plummeting straight for her.

Johnny looks up, sees it, DIVES over, TACKLES her and ROLLS.

VW impacts van. FIREBALL of combined methane and gasoline.

Jane on her back in the mud, staring up at Johnny.

JANE: Wha—?

For the briefest moment it seems as if he might kiss her, but his frustration and anger boil over. He gets up.

JOHNNY: What the fuck is going on!? (*shouts to Heaven*) What the fuck is going on!?

He turns to Jane, ranting now.

JOHNNY: You know, all my life I've been careful to stay in my own corner, looking out for number one, no complications, now suddenly I'm responsible for the *entire* fucking world and everybody and his mother is trying to kill me if my head doesn't blow up first . . . !

Jane is about to lose it, too, then claims the moral high ground.

JANE: Maybe it's not just about *you*! Not anymore.

EXT. HEAVEN. PLATFORM. NIGHT.

POV on Johnny and Jane, illuminated by flaming wreck-age. Johnny is clearly still ranting, but we don't hear him from here.

BUDDY   (*OS*): Man, you are an *idiot*!

STICK: Was an *accident*—

J-Bone appears behind them. OTHER LOTEKS are also appear-ing, clambering over container tops, attracted by the explo-sion.

J-BONE: Which onea you little—

BUDDY   (*pointing down*): Spider's van, J-Bone!

EXT. BELOW BRIDGE. NIGHT.

Johnny still ranting. Jane glaring at him.

JOHNNY: . . . and it's *my* fuckin' head they want and *my* fuckin' back you're supposed to cover and—

HEAVY METAL CAGE impacts nearby, shutting him up. STEEL CABLE attached to it SNAPS taut. They both look up to see J-Bone SLIDE quickly down the cable, hands padded with rags. J-Bone lands on top of the framework.

JANE: We have to see Jones, J-Bone! Spider sent us—

J-BONE   (*eyeing burning van*): Spider?

JANE: He's dead.

J-Bone clearly thinking Spider was inside the van.

JOHNNY: Not in that! Earlier. Get us up, okay? We gotta get to this Jones guy, fast!

J-Bone eyes Johnny suspiciously, then looks back to Jane.

J-BONE: If Spider sent you . . . (*BEAT*) Climb on.

Jane gets on, then Johnny, but just as he tries to pull himself into the cage, he winces and has to grab for an upright for support as his knees buckle. He misses the upright and almost topples over the side, but Jane grabs him just in time. Johnny tries to say something, but produces only a few UNINTELLIG-IBLE SOUNDS.

JANE: Help me!

J-Bone helps haul Johnny in. A WINCH whines, far above, as the cage rises into the dark.

EXT. HEAVEN. RAMPARTS. NIGHT.

CROWD OF LOTEKS watch as the framework is swung in. Heaven is clearly a fortified community, the Loteks armed with crossbows, etc. MURMURS of "Who's the monkey suit?" etc.

J-Bone and Jane support Johnny across a SUSPENDED WALK-WAY and into a series of loosely connected containers, toward entrance of a CABOOSE.

J-BONE: Get him in here—

INT. TAKAHASHI'S OFFICE. NIGHT.

Takahashi is preparing to leave. He takes a short JAPANESE SWORD and a CRYO-UNIT.

TAKAHASHI: My helicopter.

SECRETARY: It's waiting, sir.

Takahashi opens a case, removes an old-fashioned .357. Picks up cryo-unit and leaves. The secretary straightens a pen set, waits a beat to make sure he's really gone. She presses a button on the phone. Shinji's face appears on the screen.

SHINJI: Yes?

SECRETARY: He's on his way . . .

EXT. HEAVEN. NIGHT.

In the shadow of Heaven. Street Preacher looks up, carrying the cryo-unit on his back. His features are alight with his demented faith.

STREET PREACHER: You can run, sinners, but you can't hide . . .

He starts climbing the pylon.

INT. VILLA. STUDY. DAY.

CHILD's POV.

The same HOME MOVIE QUALITY *and ominous lighting. The same woman behind the desk, her face invisible . . .*

The POV approaching the woman, but the image bleaches and flutters again, like a film strip running out . . .

INT. HEAVEN. CONTAINER. NIGHT.

Johnny's eyes open. J-Bone is gone; only Jane is there.

JOHNNY: I saw . . . I almost saw . . . As if it was . . . a memory . . .

Jane can barely contain her relief, more that he's conscious again than anything else, but then she realizes how strong her emotions for him are and her smile disappears.

Johnny catches her expression.

JOHNNY: I'm all right.

She turns away and he realizes he misinterpreted her thoughts. He sits up, still somewhat dizzy, reaches for her. They kiss and all the danger and bottled-up fear of the last hours turns into passion.

J-BONE   (*OS*): Hey, we got a special room for that.

They let go of each other, see J-Bone grinning at them. The grin fades.

J-BONE: Time to meet Jones.

EXT. RATLANDS. NIGHT.

Three Yakuza limos arrive, park with smoking shell of Stick's VW in BACKGROUND. Shinji's ASSAULT TEAM emerges, then Shinji. Team unloads black nylon carryalls from trunks.

Shinji scanning Heaven with binoculars.

HEAVYWEIGHT opens a bag and lifts out a compact ANTI-AIRCRAFT MISSILE LAUNCHER. Hands this to his partner, a FEMALE YAKUZA, who hefts it admiringly.

FEMALE YAKUZA: Come to Momma.

She sights it, in love. Shinji lowers binoculars, turns.

SHINJI: Only if we require a diversion . . .

INT. HEAVEN. THROUGH CONTAINERS. NIGHT.

J-Bone quickly leading Johnny and Jane through containers. Living quarters, a workshop, a schoolroom made out of a school bus, even a hydroponic vegetable garden. On a GANG-WAY between two containers, Johnny accidentally knocks into a TOOL KIT with his foot, sees it FALL out of sight into the river.

J-BONE: Spider's people, they give us information, we out it—

JOHNNY: Out it?

J-BONE: Wide-band. Global. Off the commsats Jones hacks for us . . . In here . . .

INT. HEAVEN. NIGHT.

Through doorway into Lotek command central, dominated by a tree of dozens of monitors in the center. A LOTEK swings high in the air on an old converted electric chair on an extendable base, the BOOM-CHAIR, checking a monitor. Facing the monitor, central to a ragged MASS OF EQUIPMENT, is a TANK, its water clear enough to show a CREATURE inside. Big bundles of CABLES slung down into the water; SCANNER cables to PARABOLIC SCANNERS marked "U.S. NAVY," mounted high and wide apart.

Johnny stands and stares at the surreal spectacle.

EXT. HEAVEN. STRUCTURAL DETAIL. NIGHT.

CU as PITON, trailing a fine line, embeds itself in wood. The line is pulled taut.

EXT. HEAVEN. BELOW BRIDGE. NIGHT.

Shinji clips LINE-CLIMBER to end of line. Clips line-climber to his harness. FIVE harnessed HENCHMEN *also fire up lines.*

HEAVYWEIGHT: They teach you that in ninja school, Boss?

Shinji pauses, looks at his henchmen.

SHINJI: Takahashi is *mine.*

Shinji touches a button on the line-climber and rises smoothly out of sight. His henchmen follow.

INT. HEAVEN. NODE. NIGHT.

Jane's hand on glass of tank; A DOLPHIN's nose nudges the glass in greeting from inside.

J-BONE: Jones.

Johnny steps forward, puzzled. The dolphin, Jones, surfaces in a GOUT of water. Split second glimpse of Navy ARMOR.

JOHNNY: It's a . . . fish!?

JANE: *Mammal.*

The dolphin surfaces again and now stays up. The scanners SWIVEL, lock on Johnny. Johnny jumps as a scanning beam of INFRASOUND sweeps over him.

CLOSE ON JONES's *EYE.*

Targeting gear around the eye swivels; SCANNERS swivel in unison. Then scanners emit a shrill series of CLICK-

SQUEAKS—dolphin-speak. J-Bone seems to understand the sounds.

J-BONE: Yeah. Friend. How's it hangin', sailor?

J-Bone takes a hypo out of a drawer, loads it from a vial, REMOVES NEEDLE, approaches Jones.

J-BONE: He's a junkie . . . The Navy addicted 'em all to this shit . . . So they'd do the work. We give it to him now, it makes him think he's swimming.

J-Bone inserts HYPO in INJECTION VENT on Jones's armor. The dolphin quivers with pleasure, thrashing his tail languidly.

JOHNNY: And *this* was Spider's best bet . . . ?

J-BONE: One thing Spider wasn't . . . was stupid. Jones was set up to sample software out of enemy subs. Infrasound scans right through the hull.

Johnny and Jane exchange a look.

EXT. HEAVEN. GIRDERS BELOW BRIDGE. NIGHT.

Pitch dark. Street Preacher's steam-engine BREATH as he CLIMBS, the cryo-unit slung across his back. He's enormously STRONG, an irresistible force.

INT. HEAVEN. NODE. NIGHT.

Loteks are preparing the boom-chair, connecting cables.

J-BONE: He'll feed you "can-opener" codes . . .

ON JOHNNY.

Facing the chair as Loteks swing HELMET into position. We see that a conical DANGER ZONE is marked on the floor with ORANGE SPRAY PAINT.

JOHNNY: *Wait* a minute . . .

J-BONE: No *time*, friend. You're the man in a hurry.

J-Bone urges him toward chair; Johnny resists.

JOHNNY: Have you done this before? Has he? How dangerous is this?

J-Bone and his techies exchange a look.

J-BONE   (*soothingly*): Just try to keep your *head* still, okay? He's gotta triangulate the infrasound on the implant. If you move he's liable to microwave your frontal lobe . . .

JOHNNY   (*stepping back*): Forget it..

J-BONE: This way at least you got a *chance* . . . But, hey, my man, the choice is *yours*.

Johnny and Jane exchange looks; Johnny takes a deep breath and goes to the chair. Jane smiles, pleased at his decision.

Loteks lower helmet onto his head. Looks like he's ready for electrocution.

J-BONE: Give me what you've got of the download code.

Johnny produces crumpled fax. Hands it to J-Bone. The JAPA-NESE CARTOON HERO. Sits in the chair.

EXT. HEAVEN. RAMPARTS. NIGHT.

Buddy on guard duty. Shinji, like a shadow, is on him. Slits his throat and tosses him over the side. His team follows.

EXT. HEAVEN. BELOW BRIDGE. NIGHT.

Buddy's body lands with a PLOP near Heavyweight and Fe-male Yakuza. They glance over. Heavyweight saunters to-ward the corpse.

INT. HEAVEN. NODE. NIGHT.

ON A WIDE-SCREEN MONITOR. A LOTEK has fed in the code image, which fills one-third of the screen. The other two-thirds are filled with FLICKERING VIDEO SNOW. Johnny anxious to start.

JOHNNY: Let's *do* it . . .

J-BONE: Not yet. First you and I make a deal.

Johnny looks warily over to J-Bone. Now what?

J-BONE: I know what's in your head. If Jones gets it out . . . We broadcast it. Put it out, right across the planet. We *give it away.*

Johnny considers. Begins to GRIN.

JOHNNY: Listen, if you can get it out . . .

J-BONE: Yeah?

JOHNNY: Knock yourself out.

J-Bone frowns, Jane grins. Spirit of complicity. J-Bone turns to the techies.

J-BONE: Get the broadcast antennae up. Everybody clear of the infrasound area!

The Loteks scurry. Distant MECHANICAL SOUND.

Jane stays with Johnny at the chair, but J-Bone grabs her and pulls her clear of the orange-painted area.

EXT. HEAVEN. BRIDGE TOWER. NIGHT.

The massive broadcast antennae are propelled mechanically to the top of the tower.

A Yakuza helicopter drops into frame like a black dragonfly, looking for a place to put down its cargo . . .

INT. HELICOPTER. NIGHT.

Takahashi grimly looks to the PILOT, *points down. The pilot nods.*

INT. HEAVEN. NODE. NIGHT.

Johnny takes a deep breath. The scanners SWIVEL, zero on him . . . He closes his eyes, gathers himself.

JOHNNY: Now.

The scanners emit a BURST of DOLPHIN-SPEAK that SPEEDS UP to become the INFRASOUND EFFECT. Johnny goes suddenly rigid as the scan takes effect.

Jones starts to tremble in the water. Jane looks on, horrified.

ON ONE OF THE SCREENS, THE "DOLPHIN MONITOR."

Dozens of TENDRILS, very lively and organic, attempt to surround and penetrate an angular representation of Johnny's implant. They fail repeatedly, thrown off by PULSES of BLUE LIGHT.

(INFRASOUND EFFECT remains on in node until impact on page 120.)

EXT. HEAVEN. PLATFORM. NIGHT.

By the VW-bomber. Stick on duty, looking unhappy.

STICK   (*to the night, softly but bitterly*): *Big* motherfucking J-Bone almighty strategist motherfucker. Week's extra *hours* of this horseshit 'cause it was a *accident,* man, a shit fucking *accident—*

Cut off with a GASP as a crossbow bolt from one of Shinji's team finds his heart. Shinji rushes forward trying to catch him, too late. Stick falls forward across the LEVER, activating bomber.

THE SECOND VW is launched into space, WHOMP of igniting gasoline.

EXT. HEAVEN. BELOW BRIDGE. NIGHT.

Heavyweight by Buddy's body, scavenging. Sudden down-rushing FLARE of burning VW.

HEAVYWEIGHT: Wha?

VW impacts in ballooning FIREBALL, Heavyweight vanishing. The explosion partially catches Female Yakuza, hurling her into the mud, clothes and hair on fire.

She flails through mud, dragging the missile-launcher.

FEMALE YAKUZA: Yeah? *Yeah?* You think so, motherfuckers? Well, bite on *this.*

Raises the launcher to her shoulder, aiming almost straight up, and FIRES.

INT. HEAVEN. NODE. NIGHT.

Shudders with force of the explosion. The infrasound WAVERS. Johnny and Jones are oblivious to the commotion.

J-BONE: Stations! You all know the drill!

Loteks scramble to take up battle stations.

JANE: What's happening?

J-BONE: Somebody's idea of pay-back time . . .

ON AN UNWATCHED SURVEILLANCE MONITOR.

Brief flurry of violence as Shinji and his team dispatch two Loteks.

INT. HEAVEN. UNDER ROADWAY. NIGHT.

The Yakuza helicopter rises into the night, while Takahashi, carrying the cryo-unit, clambers down and drops into one of the corridors.

INT. HEAVEN. NODE. NIGHT.

Still oblivious to the battle around him, Johnny shakes in his chair, Jane by his side. Loteks running out, ready for battle. Jane torn whether to stay with Johnny or to go out and join the fray.

ON THE DOLPHIN MONITOR.

The tendrils still get repulsed. Every now and then, one penetrates slightly, but it always gets pushed back out again . . .

We MOVE IN on Johnny's face.

JOHNNY's POV.

Snatches of childhood images:

A stark, concrete modern villa, kids' toys in the driveway.

A couple of KIDS isolated in a vast landscaped garden. They're bored. A NANNY in a lawn chair listens to a Walkman.

A child's bed in a soul-less steel-and-glass room, some pictures cut from magazines on the wall.

ON THE WIDE SCREEN.

Fragments, like shadows of shapes, move in the empty spaces next to the Cartoon Hero . . .

EXT. HEAVEN. BELOW BRIDGE. NIGHT.

CU muzzle of missile-launcher.

FEMALE YAKUZA (*VO*): Eat this . . .

She fires.

INT. HEAVEN. NODE. NIGHT.

JOHNNY's *POV.*

Again, that image of the woman at her desk, her head bent over her work. This time, we almost reach the desk; the woman's head starts to lift . . .

INT. HEAVEN. CORRIDOR FROM NODE. NIGHT.

Female Yakuza's second missile DETONATES below floor, tearing a huge hole through the structure.

INT. HEAVEN. NODE. NIGHT.

Johnny is thrown from his chair, lies crumpled on the floor. Jane picks herself up from where she fell. Infrasound effect suddenly dies.

Jones submerges with a SPLASH, trailing wires and electrodes; the SUPPORT for one scanner is damaged.

Johnny opens his eyes, looks over to J-Bone, who braces himself against a console.

JOHNNY: What did you get?

Together, they look at the wide screen. Still only the Japanese Cartoon Hero, although there are some faint traces in the video snow on the other screens, faint outlines, tantalizingly close to becoming recognizable . . .

J-BONE: We didn't make it . . . (*gestures to damaged scanner*) We're not going to either . . .

J-Bone's suddenly GALVANIZED by an image on one of the SURVEILLANCE MONITORS: the automatic camera SWINGS PAST a CRUCIFIED LOTEK . . .

J-Bone rushes out of the node. Johnny didn't see the crucified Lotek.

JOHNNY: I . . . I was almost *there*, I could *feel* it starting to . . .

Defeated, Johnny sits up, still preoccupied by his own condition. Jane is about to go over to him.

TAKAHASHI (*OS*): Mr. "Smith"?

Takahashi, immaculate among the ruins, suit black as coal, cuffs white as snow, stands with the .357 hanging loosely by his side.

JOHNNY (*hopefully*): Pharmakom?

TAKAHASHI: I'm afraid not.

He whirls and SHOOTS as Jane moves, very fast. Misses. Jane finds cover behind a pile of junk.

TAKAHASHI: I must have the data.

JOHNNY: You can't shoot me—

TAKAHASHI: Not in the head . . .

He lowers the gun to the level of Johnny's gut.

Jane starts to make her move, but Takahashi is ready. He swings the gun. Jane dives back behind the junk.

Takahashi takes out the short sword with his free hand. He steps toward Johnny. The sword GLINTS; Johnny braces himself . . .

EVERY FUNCTIONING MONITOR in the node LIGHTS UP with Anna's face. The effect is of a wave of ENERGY, several of the damaged monitors simultaneously EXPLODE.

ANNA: *Takahashi!!!*

Terrible ACCUSATION in her voice. Takahashi WHIRLS around. His jaw drops.

ANNA: You don't *know* what he is carrying in his head, do you?! You are *weak,* Takahashi! *Blind! Meaningless!* You have no idea what you are returning to Pharmakom. He carries *the cure for Nerve Attenuation Syndrome.*

ON TAKAHASHI.

Powerful denial and Yakuza discipline rising to counter her. He FIRES at random into the monitors. THREE SHOTS, three SHATTERED SCREENS.

TAKAHASHI: You are a *ghost*! You are *madness*! You *lie*!!!

Anna's face CLICKS into even higher resolution.

ANNA: They had the cure one year ago, Takahashi. It was *not necessary* for your daughter to die . . .

Takahashi WINCES.

TAKAHASHI: Mikiyo . . .

ANNA: Pharmakom is keeping the cure off the market for the sake of sell-through. Treating the disease is far more profitable than curing it. Mikiyo . . .

As she says the name, she MORPHS into his daughter.

MIKIYO   (*but Anna's voice*): . . . did not need to die. (*Mikiyo's voice, in Japanese, NO SUBTITLES*) *Please father, listen to her!*

Takahashi fires THREE REMAINING ROUNDS into main CONTROL PANEL. Throwing down the .357, he takes a formal two-handed grip on sword and CLEAVES cables leading to panel, a ZEN SWING. Sparks fly; Anna vanishes as all the monitors go black.

TAKAHASHI's FACE alight with MAD, TRAGIC TRIUMPH. He turns back to Johnny, raises his sword; then his entire body SPASMS.

He sinks to his knees and pitches forward, revealing Shinji, who holsters the air gun and takes out his filament. A SECOND YAKUZA faces off with Jane, aiming his air gun.

SHINJI: Hello, Johnny . . .

ZZIP! The filament slices an ellipse from the metal junk where Johnny's head should have been. Johnny backs up; his fingers find a CROWBAR among the junk. He brandishes it like a weapon. ZINGG! He is holding a twelve-inch stump with a MIRROR-POLISHED end.

SHINJI: Raise your chin. Let's make this clean.

Second Yakuza aiming across the waist-high console between Jane and him. As he fires, she DROPS. Darts SPATTER off the metal console, missing her.

Jane SCISSORS her legs as she pulls herself below the console and through, catching Second Yakuza's legs, dropping him.

Johnny quickly backing away out of node over ANOTHER CONTAINER. Shinji pursues, filament poised.

Jane throws herself on Second Yakuza, driving her FIST into his throat; his air gun slides across the floor, Jane frantically clawing after it—

INT. HEAVEN. CONTAINER. NIGHT.

Johnny backs up into a messy storage container, filled with electronics and other salvaged junk. Not much room to move and no way out. Shinji lets fly with the filament; Johnny dives out of the way. The filament cuts through a stack of rusted metal junk, barely moving it. Johnny crawls up, backs against the wall. Shinji moves forward . . .

EXT. HEAVEN. BELOW BRIDGE. NIGHT.

Female Yakuza fires . . .

INT. HEAVEN. CONTAINER. NIGHT.

The missile DETONATES at the JOINT to the next container. The container tilts down majestically until it hangs vertical, swinging from CREAKING, PROTESTING hawsers. Johnny is almost thrown out into the river, manages to hang on to a protruding GIRDER, DANGLING in space.

Shinji has managed to grab hold of the post of some built-in shelves. He scrambles down toward Johnny, who thinks it's all over for him.

SHINJI: Hold on!

Johnny looks at him. He gets it. Gives a crazed WHOOP of LAUGHTER.

JOHNNY: If I fall you don't get the head, right? You lose the head, you're fucked!

Shinji, sweating bullets, leans down, extends his hand . . .

INT. HEAVEN. NODE. NIGHT.

Jane, the Second Yakuza's air gun in hand; his corpse is at her feet. She starts after Johnny . . .

STREET PREACHER (*OS*): Jesus time.

Street Preacher blocks her path.

INT. HEAVEN. CONTAINER. NIGHT.

ON JOHNNY's WRIST.

As Shinji's hand closes around it. Johnny looks up, GRINS and lets go with his other hand, reaching up to grab the lapel of Shinji's suit, pulling him over.

Shinji falls, manages to grab the same girder.

They dangle next to each other, Shinji closest to the END OF THE GIRDER, frantically treading air.

BELOW THEM.

Bits of junk falling into darkness, past their legs . . .

Johnny is SLUGGING Shinji in the face with his free hand. He's too close to do much real damage, but he's so PISSED OFF, he no longer cares about his own safety. Shinji, we see to our considerable satisfaction, is TERRIFIED.

Johnny stops punching Shinji, SCREAMS his fury, swings his body back and SLAMS into Shinji, trying to dislodge him. Shinji is holding on, tries frantically to climb atop the girder.

ON JOHNNY as he lets go with one hand and grabs the THUMB TIP, pulling it toward him . . .

SHINJI's EYES, wide with surprise.

Johnny brings the FILAMENT down THROUGH the girder, slicing through it . . .

Their eyes meet in the instant of Shinji's recognition of his fate—then Shinji and the girder tip plummet from sight . . .

Shinji SCREAMS as he and the girder tip head for the river, his scream DOPPLERING down until it's INSTANTLY cut off on impact with the unseen river below.

Johnny hangs on, as if he can't remember what he's doing there. The OMINOUS CREAKING OF STRAINED HAWSERS . . . A cable SNAPS; the container ROCKS . . .

He pulls himself together, starts to struggle up into the container.

INT. HEAVEN. NODE. NIGHT.

CRASH . . . as Street Preacher hurls Jane back against the lockers with such force they buckle slightly. Her eyes ROLL UP and she flops forward. Street Preacher catches her. With one hand hooked in the waistband of her jeans, he drags her, face and boots scraping, across the floor, to where the explosion has left two heavy timbers handily arranged in the form of a big, rough wooden CROSS. He slams her up against the cross . . .

EXT. HEAVEN. RAMPARTS. NIGHT.

J-Bone kneels, adjusting the laser sight he took from Henson on his air bow. He aims down . . .

EXT. HEAVEN. BELOW BRIDGE. NIGHT.

Female Yakuza aiming again. A red dot searches over her body, comes to rest on her forehead . . . A BOLT PLANTS itself in the exact spot. Expression of surprise as she keels forward.

INT. HEAVEN. NODE. NIGHT.

Johnny emerges from the container, still trembling with adrenaline and horror. Takahashi stands in front of him, swaying on his feet, his hand inside his coat. Johnny is too wrecked to do anything but stare. Takahashi's face is horribly distorted in pain, his shirt drenched in blood. He takes his hand from his jacket, produces IMAGE #2, the RIOTS SCENE, crumpled, wet with his own blood.

TAKAHASHI: Yours . . .

Johnny takes it. Stares in wonder as Takahashi sinks to his knees and dies. Stares at the image. Then he hears SINGING, a tuneless hymn of death . . .

STREET PREACHER   (*OS*): In the blood, in the blood, in the sweet everlasting blood of the Lamb . . .

Street Preacher holding a SPIKE above Jane's outstretched palm, raising a hammer, the crucifixion about to begin . . .

STREET PREACHER: Jesus is waiting . . .

The HAMMER comes down . . . Jane SCREAMS in pain, just as Johnny smashes Street Preacher in the back of the head with a piece of metal junk. Street Preacher staggers, dropping nail and hammer, recovers instantly, whirls, knife lashing for Johnny's neck. Johnny barely blocks it with the junk. He staggers. Street Preacher easily lifts him and HURLS him headfirst into the wall.

CLOSE ON JOHNNY's FACE.

Screwed up with pain.

His POV of the node. Odd angle as he sinks to the floor . . .

ANOTHER MEMORY FLASH.

Of the study, moving toward the woman. The POV reaches the desk. The woman looks up; her face is FEATURELESS, as if erased. The voice is MECHANICALLY distorted, slightly too slow.

VOICE: Bad boy!

A small hand reaches for a picture frame between them. The woman reaches to prevent him. The picture falls. The POV looks down at the floor, to the fallen picture, faceup. A smiling Anna as the perfect mother, a baby in her arms. POV moves in quickly on face, CROPPING the picture, the CLICK of the UPLOAD REMOTE as it morphs into Anna in Beijing, the THIRD IMAGE . . .

ON JOHNNY.

As he scrambles to his feet; look of AMAZEMENT on his face.

Street Preacher advances, Johnny backing up, leading him away from Jane.

JOHNNY: I've got it . . . Got it now . . .

STREET PREACHER: He has made you the vessel of His mercy . . . As I am the vessel of His wrath . . .

JOHNNY: You don't understand! I've got the third image!

Johnny backing through node, Street Preacher stalking him, sure of the kill.

Jane has grabbed hold of the nail through her other hand, clenches her teeth. PULLS hard. Wrenches it loose . . .

Johnny makes a last desperate attempt to stop Street Preacher with a lightning combination: hard kick at his knees. Like kicking a lamppost. A short right to a rock-hard midsection. Street Preacher back-fists him across the floor. Johnny stays down.

Jane approaches in BG; she's in worse shape than Johnny. In pain. She limps/stumbles toward dolphin tank.

STREET PREACHER: The cure is mine, sinner . . .

As Jane reaches tank. Presses her bloody palm against glass. Jones's eye appears.

JANE: Jones . . .

Leaves a bloody palm-print on glass.

CLOSE ON JONES's EYE, gizmo's swiveling . . .

Street Preacher lovingly positions Johnny for efficient decapi-tation. Johnny seems to have given up.

Jane climbing support to broken scanner. An amazing feat, considering her condition.

Street Preacher raises his knife.

Jane, on scanner tower, LIFTS scanner into position with her injured hand.

Street Preacher starts the DOWNSTROKE . . .

JANE: *Jones!!!*

INFRASOUND powers up. Street Preacher looks up as the scanners come to life, start to move. His eyes go to the tank, Jones.

STREET PREACHER: What spawn of Satan—

JANE: *Now!*

As INFRASOUND reaches new painful level and the scanners SWING in UNISON . . .

TRACKING the quick progress of an invisible POINT OF DE-STRUCTION as it moves smoothly and inexorably through a litter of small objects in its path, destroying each in turn: a beer bottle EXPLODES; SMOKE curls from a small electronic de-vice; the image on a small video game goes CRAZY . . .

Culminating on Street Preacher's HEAD . . .

He SCREAMS.

All over his body, his implants EXPLODE.

Johnny summons EVERYTHING and lunges up, SMASHING Street Preacher in the face, toppling him backward into the cables that Takahashi cut earlier.

Street Preacher ROARS in pain and rage. He grabs the end of a cut cable and pulls himself upright, his huge HAND reaching for Johnny, who grabs a second cut cable and tosses it to Street Preacher, who catches it instinctively . . .

BLUE-WHITE CURRENT surges through him, smoke curling from his clothes, RESTORING POWER to the node. The monitors LIGHT UP again.

Street Preacher's body falls back to the floor, his hands still clutching the cables.

Jane CRASHES from scanner support. Johnny stumbles toward her as J-Bone enters the node. Johnny kneels next to Jane.

JANE: I'm okay . . .

Johnny turns to J-Bone, a new determination in his eyes.

JOHNNY: Hook me up! I've got it!

Johnny's hands tremble as he scans in Image #2. The Riots Scene appears next to the Cartoon Hero on the wide screen.

J-BONE: Where's number *three*?!

JOHNNY: In my *head*!

Johnny rushes to the chair.

INT. HEAVEN. NODE. NIGHT.

A NUMBER OF MONITORS flicker and Anna apears on them, stopping Johnny in his tracks. Her images seem damaged, blue flames licking at the lower corners, as if her powers are fading. He stares, her significance to him taking more concrete shape by the moment. Her eyes are on him, intense, expectant . . .

JOHNNY: You're . . . in my memory . . . somewhere . . . It feels like . . . like you're my . . .

He stops, the emotion blocked.

ANNA: Your *mother.* I *am* your mother. I was obsessed with building Pharmakom. Later, when you had your childhood erased, it was too late for me to . . . Now I have this final chance.

Johnny's emotions in utter conflict. Finally:

JOHNNY: If you're my *mother . . . . , why* didn't you tell me you were the third image?!

Anna winces, hurt. A few more monitors flicker and her image disappears from them.

ANNA: Because I did not *know.* I had no *access!* I arranged that they should choose you, because . . . I have *always* watched you, Johnny . . .

Jane's staring at Anna, fascinated.

J-BONE: Hey! We're gonna do the download, we do it *now,* okay? We're losing power . . . !

Anna's image FLUCTUATES. Her image disappears from a few more monitors. Johnny looks to J-Bone. Back to Anna. Old hurt and disappointment in his face. In this moment he is the baffled, neglected child. Then he steps toward the chair, picks up the downloader helmet.

JOHNNY: I've got to do this.

Jane helps him put on the helmet. J-Bone winces, studying dials next to a monitor with data.

J-BONE: One problem. If we take it out easy, it's gonna be garbage because of the seepage. If we loop it through Jones, we save the cure ... but it's the neurological equivalent of bungee jumping through a brick wall; it'll probably kill you.

ANNA   (*frantic*): Johnny, I never meant to—

ON JOHNNY. Looking at Anna's image, back to Jane. BEAT. Turns to J-Bone.

JOHNNY: Loop it.

JANE: Johnny ...

He reaches out to her, then turns to J-Bone.

JOHNNY: *Hit me.*

J-Bone throwing switches. White sparks cascade from video-tree. Street Preacher STEAMS, sparks snapping around his corpse. Jones surfaces with a SPLASH.

ON THE WIDE SCREEN.

As Anna's Beijing image takes its place next to the others ...

J-BONE: Here we go ...

He flicks another switch.

INT. HEAVEN. NODE. NIGHT.

Johnny SPASMS as the download begins. Jones THRASHES in the tank, water flying. Jane takes Johnny's hands.

Anna watches Johnny throughout . . .

ON DOLPHIN MONITOR.

The IMPLANT REPRESENTATION OPENS, unfolding hypnotically . . .

J-Bone swivels to face a bank of CAMERAS, throwing switches. Suddenly, his image appears on all of the monitors (except the tryptich).

ON THE MONITORS.

J-BONE: Listen up, world, this is your last blast from Lotek World Headquarters and we're going out with a *bang*! So hit that VCR *now*, people, cause we got the *cure* for NAS, that's right, a surefire cure for the shakes, coming *now*, coming *at* you, hot from the labs at Pharmakom, that's right, *Pharmakom*, world's third largest corporation, and, no, they didn't *want* you to get it, but here it *is*—

He throws a switch.

ON THE DOLPHIN MONITOR as the unfolding implant turns into a RUSH through CYBERSPACE of the Pharmakom data . . .

PHARMAKOM DATA cascades across the screens . . .

ALL AROUND THE WORLD.

A MONTAGE, showing the data on all TV screens and monitors, in labs, living rooms, tents of nomads, windows of video stores, screen-walls of Shibuya skyscrapers . . . ASTONISHED AUDIENCES . . .

BACK IN THE NODE.

Johnny, straining in the downloader, almost there . . . almost DEAD . . . He opens his eyes for a second, the pain in them approaching panic. His eyes meet Jane's for a moment. Like a good-bye.

JANE: Johnny . . .

He squeezes his eyes shut again.

INT. HEAVEN. NODE. NIGHT.

Johnny slumps down in his chair, seemingly lifeless. As almost all of the live monitors EXPLODE in a SHOWER OF SPARKS, J-Bone gives a mighty WHOOP of glee!

J-BONE: *Done!* It belongs to *everybody* now! *Done!*

Jane looks at Johnny, limp in the chair, seemingly dead, rushes over.

ON ANNA's SAD EYES.

On one of the few surviving monitors, her image still deteriorating, the blue flames licking their way up.

ANNA: I built a world. There was *always* a place in it for you—

Johnny's eyelids flutter, then open at the sound of her voice; pulled back from the grave.

ON JANE, hardly able to contain her relief.

He looks up at Anna. Gathers strength.

JOHNNY: Lady—*I voted with my feet.*

Stung, Anna cringes.

ANNA: But I was—

JOHNNY: *Remember?*

LONG BEAT. Anna's image rapidly deteriorating.

ANNA: Johnny! The Pharmakom board! They are erasing me! Burning me out of the mainframe!

Johnny turns his eyes away from her. He's silently CRYING.

ANNA   (*OS*): Johnny, speak to me! Johnny, *you're my son!!* Why *don't you look at me!!*

JOHNNY: I'm not . . . There's nothing inside. Not what you want . . .

ANNA: JOHNNEEEEeeeee—

The digital flames undo her, leaving HISSING, SILVER STATIC.

Jane is shaken.

JANE: Was she really . . . ?

BEAT as Johnny tries to come to grips with his emotions.

JOHNNY: I don't know . . . I guess I . . . never did.

From outside a distant RACKET is rising. J-Bone struggles through the wreckage, heaves aside a section of tarp, opening a gap into the night.

EMERGENCY FLARES lift from the city, float down. SIRENS, CAR HORNS, GUNS FIRING. Someone cuts loose with a STAR SHELL, a pretty Disneyland light-flower blossoming over the frozen hell of Newark.

Johnny and Jane, propping each other up, join J-Bone, gazing out, baffled.

Street Preacher starts to rise behind them . . .

JOHNNY: What's going on?

J-BONE: *Celebrating.* They *know.* Got our message.

Street Preacher closes in on them . . .

J-Bone turns, raising air bow. THWACK! A bolt buries itself in Street Preacher's heart. He falls back.

J-Bone smiles. Saintly.

J-BONE: Said it's *over.*

They turn back to celebration. CAMERA moves past them into one of the very few monitors still going, the WIDE SCREEN of the Three Images: the Cartoon Hero, the Riots and Anna.

ROLL CREDITS OVER THIS.

The Story

I put the shotgun in an Adidas bag and padded it out with four pairs of tennis socks, not my style at all, but that was what I was aiming for: If they think you're crude, go technical; if they think you're technical, go crude. I'm a very technical boy. So I decided to get as crude as possible. These days, though, you have to be pretty technical before you can even aspire to crudeness. I'd had to turn both these twelve-gauge shells from brass stock, on a lathe, and then load them myself; I'd had to dig up an old microfiche with instructions for hand-loading cartridges; I'd had to build a lever-action press to seat the primers—all very tricky. But I knew they'd work.

The meet was set for the Drome at 2300, but I rode the tube three stops past the closest platform and walked back. Immaculate procedure.

I checked myself out in the chrome siding of a coffee kiosk, your basic sharp-faced Caucasoid with a ruff of stiff, dark hair. The girls at Under the Knife were big on Sony Mao, and it was getting harder to keep them from adding the chic suggestion of epicanthic folds. It probably wouldn't fool Ralfi Face, but it might get me next to his table.

The Drome is a single narrow space with a bar down one side and tables along the other, thick with pimps and handlers and an arcane array of dealers. The Magnetic Dog Sisters were on the door that night, and I didn't relish trying to get out past them if things didn't work out. They were two meters tall and thin as greyhounds. One was black and the other white, but aside from that they were as nearly identical as cosmetic surgery could make them. They'd been lovers for years and were bad news in a tussle. I was never quite sure which one had originally been male.

Ralfi was sitting at his usual table. Owing me a lot of money. I had hundreds of megabytes stashed in my head on an idiot/savant basis, information I had no conscious access to. Ralfi had left it there. He hadn't, however, come back for it. Only Ralfi could retrieve the data, with a code phrase of his own invention. I'm not cheap to begin with, but my overtime on storage is astronomical. And Ralfi had been very scarce.

Then I'd heard that Ralfi Face wanted to put out a contract on me. So I'd arranged to meet him in the Drome, but I'd arranged it as Edward Bax, clandestine importer, late of Rio and Peking.

The Drome stank of biz, a metallic tang of nervous tension. Muscle-boys scattered through the crowd were flexing stock parts at one another and trying on thin, cold grins, some of them so lost under superstructures of muscle graft that their outlines weren't really human.

Pardon me. Pardon me, friends. Just Eddie Bax here, Fast Eddie the Importer, with his professionally nondescript gym bag, and please ignore this slit, just wide enough to admit his right hand.

Ralfi wasn't alone. Eighty kilos of blond California beef perched alertly in the chair next to his, martial arts written all over him.

Fast Eddie Bax was in the chair opposite them before the beef's hands were off the table. "You black belt?" I asked eagerly. He nodded, blue eyes running an automatic scanning pattern between my eyes and my hands. "Me, too," I said. "Got mine here in the bag." And I shoved my hand through the slit and thumbed the safety off. Click. "Double twelve-gauge with the triggers wired together."

"That's a gun," Ralfi said, putting a plump, restraining hand on his boy's taut blue nylon chest. "Johnny has an antique firearm in his bag." So much for Edward Bax.

I guess he'd always been Ralfi Something or Other, but he owed his acquired surname to a singular vanity. Built something like an overripe pear, he'd worn the once-famous face of Christian White for twenty years—Christian White of the Aryan Reggae Band, Sony Mao to his generation, and final champion of race rock. I'm a whiz at trivia.

Christian White: classic pop face with a singer's high-definition muscles, chiseled cheekbones. Angelic in one light, handsomely depraved in another. But Ralfi's eyes lived behind that face, and they were small and cold and black.

"Please," he said, "let's work this out like businessmen." His voice was marked by a horrible prehensile sincerity, and the corners of his beautiful Christian White mouth were always wet. "Lewis here," nodding in the beefboy's direction, "is a meatball." Lewis took this impassively, looking like something built from a kit. "You aren't a meatball, Johnny."

"Sure I am, Ralfi, a nice meatball chock-full of implants where you can store your dirty laundry while you go off shopping for people to kill me. From my end of this bag, Ralfi, it looks like you've got some explaining to do."

"It's this last batch of product, Johnny." He sighed deeply. "In my role as broker—"

"Fence," I corrected.

"As broker, I'm usually very careful as to sources."

"You buy only from those who steal the best. Got it."

He sighed again. "I try," he said wearily, "not to buy from fools. This time, I'm afraid, I've done that." Third sigh was the cue for Lewis to trigger the neural disruptor they'd taped under my side of the table.

I put everything I had into curling the index finger of my right hand, but I no longer seemed to be connected to it. I could feel the metal of the gun and the foam-pad tape I'd wrapped around the stubby grip, but my hands were cool wax, distant and inert. I was hoping Lewis was a true meatball, thick enough to go for the gym bag and snag my rigid trigger finger, but he wasn't.

"We've been very worried about you, Johnny. Very worried. You see, that's Yakuza property you have there. A fool took it from them, Johnny. A dead fool."

Lewis giggled.

It all made sense then, an ugly kind of sense, like bags of wet sand settling around my head. Killing wasn't Ralfi's style. Lewis wasn't even Ralfi's style. But he'd got himself stuck between the Sons of the Neon Chrysanthemum and something that belonged to

them—or, more likely, something of theirs that belonged to someone else. Ralfi, of course, could use the code phrase to throw me
into idiot/savant, and I'd spill their hot program without remembering a single quarter tone. For a fence like Ralfi, that would ordi-
narily have been enough. But not for the Yakuza. The Yakuza would
know about Squids, for one thing, and they wouldn't want to worry
about one lifting those dim and permanent traces of their program
out of my head. I didn't know very much about Squids, but I'd
heard stories, and I made it a point never to repeat them to my
clients. No, the Yakuza wouldn't like that; it looked too much like
evidence. They hadn't got where they were by leaving evidence
around. Or alive.

Lewis was grinning. I think he was visualizing a point just
behind my forehead and imagining how he could get there the
hard way.

"Hey," said a low voice, feminine, from somewhere behind my
right shoulder, "you cowboys sure aren't having too lively a time."

"Pack it, bitch," Lewis said, his tanned face very still. Ralfi
looked blank.

"Lighten up. You want to buy some good freebase?" She pulled
up a chair and quickly sat before either of them could stop her. She
was barely inside my fixed field of vision, a thin girl with mirrored
glasses, her dark hair cut in a rough shag. She wore black leather,
open over a T-shirt slashed diagonally with stripes of red and black.
"Eight thou a gram weight."

Lewis snorted his exasperation and tried to slap her out of the
chair. Somehow he didn't quite connect, and her hand came up
and seemed to brush his wrist as it passed. Bright blood sprayed the
table. He was clutching his wrist white-knuckle tight, blood trickling
from between his fingers.

But hadn't her hand been empty?

He was going to need a tendon stapler. He stood up carefully,
without bothering to push his chair back. The chair toppled backward, and he stepped out of my line of sight without a word.

"He better get a medic to look at that," she said. "That's a
nasty cut."

"You have no idea," said Ralfi, suddenly sounding very tired, "the depths of shit you have just gotten yourself into."

"No kidding? Mystery. I get real excited by mysteries. Like why your friend here's so quiet. Frozen, like. Or what this thing here is for," and she held up the little control unit that she'd somehow taken from Lewis. Ralfi looked ill.

"You, ah, want maybe a quarter-million to give me that and take a walk?" A fat hand came up to stroke his pale, lean face nervously.

"What I want," she said, snapping her fingers so that the unit spun and glittered, "is work. A job. Your boy hurt his wrist. But a quarter'll do for a retainer."

Ralfi let his breath out explosively and began to laugh, exposing teeth that hadn't been kept up to the Christian White standard. Then she turned the disruptor off.

"Two million," I said.

"My kind of man," she said, and laughed. "What's in the bag?"

"A shotgun."

"Crude." It might have been a compliment.

Ralfi said nothing at all.

"Name's Millions. Molly Millions. You want to get out of here, boss? People are starting to stare." She stood up. She was wearing leather jeans the color of dried blood.

And I saw for the first time that the mirrored lenses were surgical inlays, the silver rising smoothly from her high cheekbones, sealing her eyes in their sockets. I saw my new face twinned there.

"I'm Johnny," I said. "We're taking Mr. Face with us."

He was outside, waiting. Looking like your standard tourist tech, in plastic zoris and a silly Hawaiian shirt printed with blowups of his firm's most popular microprocessor; a mild little guy, the kind most likely to wind up drunk on sake in a bar that puts out miniature rice crackers with seaweed garnish. He looked like the kind who sing the corporate anthem and cry, who shake hands endlessly with the bartender. And the pimps and the dealers would leave him alone, pegging him as innately conservative. Not up for much, and careful with his credit when he was.

The way I figured it later, they must have amputated part of his left thumb, somewhere behind the first joint, replacing it with a prosthetic tip, and cored the stump, fitting it with a spool and socket molded from one of the Ono-Sendai diamond analogs. Then they'd carefully wound the spool with three meters of monomolecular filament.

Molly got into some kind of exchange with the Magnetic Dog Sisters, giving me a chance to usher Ralfi through the door with the gym bag pressed lightly against the base of his spine. She seemed to know them. I heard the black one laugh.

I glanced up, out of some passing reflex, maybe because I've never got used to it, to the soaring arcs of light and the shadows of the geodesics above them. Maybe that saved me.

Ralfi kept walking, but I don't think he was trying to escape. I think he'd already given up. Probably he already had an idea of what we were up against.

I looked back down in time to see him explode.

Playback on full recall shows Ralfi stepping forward as the little tech sidles out of nowhere, smiling. Just a suggestion of a bow, and his left thumb falls off. It's a conjuring trick. The thumb hangs suspended. Mirrors? Wires? And Ralfi stops, his back to us, dark crescents of sweat under the armpits of his pale summer suit. He knows. He must have known. And then the joke-shop thumbtip, heavy as lead, arcs out in a lightning yo-yo trick, and the invisible thread connecting it to the killer's hand passes laterally through Ralfi's skull, just above his eyebrows, whips up, and descends, slicing the pear-shaped torso diagonally from shoulder to rib cage. Cuts so fine that no blood flows until synapses misfire and the first tremors surrender the body to gravity.

Ralfi tumbled apart in a pink cloud of fluids, the three mismatched sections rolling forward onto the tiled pavement. In total silence.

I brought the gym bag up, and my hand convulsed. The recoil nearly broke my wrist.

It must have been raining; ribbons of water cascaded from a ruptured geodesic and spattered on the tile behind us. We crouched in the narrow gap between a surgical boutique and an antique shop. She'd just edged one mirrored eye around the corner to report a single Volks module in front of the Drome, red lights flashing. They were sweeping Ralfi up. Asking questions.

I was covered in scorched white fluff. The tennis socks. The gym bag was a ragged plastic cuff around my wrist. "I don't see how the hell I missed him."

" 'Cause he's fast, so fast." She hugged her knees and rocked back and forth on her bootheels. "His nervous system's jacked up. He's factory custom." She grinned and gave a little squeal of delight. "I'm gonna get that boy. Tonight. He's the best, number one, top dollar, state of the art."

"What you're going to get, for this boy's two million, is my ass out of here. Your boyfriend back there was mostly grown in a vat in Chiba City. He's a Yakuza assassin."

"Chiba. Yeah. See, Molly's been Chiba, too." And she showed me her hands, fingers slightly spread. Her fingers were slender, tapered, very white against the polished burgundy nails. Ten blades snicked straight out from their recesses beneath her nails, each one a narrow, double-edged scalpel in pale blue steel.

I'd never spent much time in Nighttown. Nobody there had anything to pay me to remember, and most of them had a lot they paid regularly to forget. Generations of sharpshooters had chipped away at the neon until the maintenance crews gave up. Even at noon the arcs were soot-black against faintest pearl.

Where do you go when the world's wealthiest criminal order is feeling for you with calm, distant fingers? Where do you hide from the Yakuza, so powerful that it owns comsats and at least three shuttles? The Yakuza is a true multinational, like ITT and Ono-Sendai. Fifty years before I was born the Yakuza had already absorbed the Triads, the Mafia, the Union Corse.

Molly had an answer: you hide in the Pit, in the lowest circle, where any outside influence generates swift, concentric ripples of raw menace. You hide in Nighttown. Better yet, you hide *above* Nighttown, because the Pit's inverted, and the bottom of its bowl touches the sky, the sky that Nighttown never sees, sweating under its own firmament of acrylic resin, up where the Lo Teks crouch in the dark like gargoyles, black-market cigarettes dangling from their lips.

She had another answer, too.

"So you're locked up good and tight, Johnny-san? No way to get that program without the password?" She led me into the shadows that waited beyond the bright tube platform. The concrete walls were overlaid with graffiti, years of them twisting into a single metascrawl of rage and frustration.

"The stored data are fed in through a modified series of micro-surgical contraautism prostheses." I reeled off a numb version of my standard sales pitch. "Client's code is stored in a special chip; barring Squids, which we in the trade don't like to talk about, there's no way to recover your phrase. Can't drug it out, cut it out, torture it. I don't *know* it, never did."

"Squids? Crawly things with arms?" We emerged into a deserted street market. Shadowy figures watched us from across a makeshift square littered with fish heads and rotting fruit.

"Superconducting quantum interference detectors. Used them in the war to find submarines, suss out enemy cyber systems."

"Yeah? Navy stuff? From the war? Squid'll read that chip of yours?" She'd stopped walking, and I felt her eyes on me behind those twin mirrors.

"Even the primitive models could measure a magnetic field a billionth the strength of geomagnetic force; it's like pulling a whisper out of a cheering stadium."

"Cops can do that already, with parabolic microphones and lasers."

"But your data's still secure." Pride in profession. "No government'll let their cops have Squids, not even the security heavies. Too much chance of interdepartmental funnies; they're too likely to watergate you."

"Navy stuff," she said, and her grin gleamed in the shadows. "Navy stuff. I got a friend down here who was in the navy, name's Jones. I think you'd better meet him. He's a junkie, though. So we'll have to take him something."

"A junkie?"

"A dolphin."

He was more than a dolphin, but from another dolphin's point of view he might have seemed like something less. I watched him swirling sluggishly in his galvanized tank. Water slopped over the side, wetting my shoes. He was surplus from the last war. A cyborg.

He rose out of the water, showing us the crusted plates along his sides, a kind of visual pun, his grace nearly lost under articulated armor, clumsy and prehistoric. Twin deformities on either side of his skull had been engineered to house sensor units. Silver lesions gleamed on exposed sections of his gray-white hide.

Molly whistled. Jones thrashed his tail, and more water cascaded down the side of the tank.

"What is this place?" I peered at vague shapes in the dark, rusting chain link and things under tarps. Above the tank hung a clumsy wooden framework, crossed and recrossed by rows of dusty Christmas lights.

"Funland. Zoo and carnival rides. 'Talk with the War Whale.' All that. Some whale Jones is. . . ."

Jones reared again and fixed me with a sad and ancient eye.

"How's he talk?" Suddenly I was anxious to go.

"That's the catch. Say 'hi,' Jones."

And all the bulbs lit simultaneously. They were flashing red, white, and blue.

RWBRWBRWB
RWBRWBRWB
RWBRWBRWB
RWBRWBRWB
RWBRWBRWB

"Good with symbols, see, but the code's restricted. In the navy they had him wired into an audiovisual display." She drew the narrow package from a jacket pocket. "Pure shit, Jones. Want it?" He froze in the water and started to sink. I felt a strange panic, remembering that he wasn't a fish, that he could drown. "We want the key to Johnny's bank, Jones. We want it fast."

The lights flickered, died.

"Go for it, Jones!"

B
BBBBBBBBB
B
B
B

Blue bulbs, cruciform.
Darkness.
"Pure! It's *clean*. Come on, Jones."

WWWWWWWWW
WWWWWWWWW
WWWWWWWWW
WWWWWWWWW
WWWWWWWWW

White sodium glare washed her features, stark monochrome, shadows cleaving from her cheekbones.

```
R    RRRRR
R    R
R    R
RRRRRRRRR
        R    R
        R    R
RRRRR    R
```

The arms of the red swastika were twisted in her silver glasses. "Give it to him," I said. "We've got it."

Ralfi Face. No imagination.

Jones heaved half his armored bulk over the edge of his tank, and I thought the metal would give way. Molly stabbed him overhand with the Syrette, driving the needle between two plates. Propellant hissed. Patterns of light exploded, spasming across the frame and then fading to black.

We left him drifting, rolling languorously in the dark water. Maybe he was dreaming of his war in the Pacific, of the cyber mines he'd swept, nosing gently into their circuitry with the Squid he'd used to pick Ralfi's pathetic password from the chip buried in my head.

"I can see them slipping up when he was demobbed, letting him out of the navy with that gear intact, but how does a cybernetic dolphin get wired to smack?"

"The war," she said. "They all were. Navy did it. How else you get 'em working for you?"

"I'm not sure this profiles as good business," the pirate said, angling for better money. "Target specs on a comsat that isn't in the book—"

"Waste my time and you won't profile at all," said Molly, leaning across his scarred plastic desk to prod him with her forefinger.

"So maybe you want to buy your microwaves somewhere else?" He was a tough kid, behind his Mao-job. A Nighttowner by birth, probably.

Her hand blurred down the front of his jacket, completely severing a lapel without even rumpling the fabric.

"So we got a deal or not?"

"Deal," he said, staring at his ruined lapel with what he must have hoped was only polite interest. "Deal."

While I checked the two recorders we'd bought, she extracted the slip of paper I'd given her from the zippered wrist pocket of her jacket. She unfolded it and read silently, moving her lips. She shrugged. "This is it?"

"Shoot," I said, punching the RECORD studs of the two decks simultaneously.

"Christian White," she recited, "and his Aryan Reggae Band."

Faithful Ralfi, a fan to his dying day.

Transition to idiot/savant mode is always less abrupt than I expect it to be. The pirate broadcaster's front was a failing travel agency in a pastel cube that boasted a desk, three chairs, and a faded poster of a Swiss orbital spa. A pair of toy birds with blown-glass bodies and tin legs were sipping monotonously from a Styrofoam cup of water on a ledge beside Molly's shoulder. As I phased into mode, they accelerated gradually until their Day-Glo-feathered crowns became solid arcs of color. The LEDs that told seconds on the plastic wall clock had become meaningless pulsing grids, and Molly and the Mao-faced boy grew hazy, their arms blurring occasionally in insect-quick ghosts of gesture. And then it all faded to cool gray static and an endless tone poem in an artificial language.

I sat and sang dead Ralfi's stolen program for three hours.

The mall runs forty kilometers from end to end, a ragged overlap of Fuller domes roofing what was once a suburban artery. If they turn off the arcs on a clear day, a gray approximation of sunlight filters through layers of acrylic, a view like the prison sketches of Giovanni Piranesi. The three southernmost kilometers roof Nighttown. Nighttown pays no taxes, no utilities. The neon arcs are dead, and the geodesics have been smoked black by decades of cooking fires. In the nearly total darkness of a Nighttown noon, who notices a few dozen mad children lost in the rafters?

We'd been climbing for two hours, up concrete stairs and

steel ladders with perforated rungs, past abandoned gantries and dust-covered tools. We'd started in what looked like a disused maintenance yard, stacked with triangular roofing segments. Everything there had been covered with that same uniform layer of spraybomb graffiti: gang names, initials, dates back to the turn of the century. The graffiti followed us up, gradually thinning until a single name was repeated at intervals. LO TEK. In dripping black capitals.

"Who's Lo Tek?"

"Not us, boss." She climbed a shivering aluminum ladder and vanished through a hole in a sheet of corrugated plastic. "'Low technique, low technology.'" The plastic muffled her voice. I followed her up, nursing my aching wrist. "Lo Teks, they'd think that shotgun trick of yours was effete."

An hour later I dragged myself up through another hole, this one sawed crookedly in a sagging sheet of plywood, and met my first Lo Tek.

"'S okay," Molly said, her hand brushing my shoulder. "It's just Dog. Hey, Dog."

In the narrow beam of her taped flash, he regarded us with his one eye and slowly extruded a thick length of grayish tongue, licking huge canines. I wondered how they wrote off tooth-bud transplants from Dobermans as low technology. Immunosuppressives don't exactly grow on trees.

"Moll." Dental augmentation impeded his speech. A string of saliva dangled from his twisted lower lip. "Heard ya comin'. Long time." He might have been fifteen, but the fangs and a bright mosaic of scars combined with the gaping socket to present a mask of total bestiality. It had taken time and a certain kind of creativity to assemble that face, and his posture told me he enjoyed living behind it. He wore a pair of decaying jeans, black with grime and shiny along the creases. His chest and feet were bare. He did something with his mouth that approximated a grin. "Bein' followed, you."

Far off, down in Nighttown, a water vendor cried his trade.

"Strings jumping, Dog?" She swung her flash to the side, and I saw thin cords tied to eyebolts, cords that ran to the edge and vanished.

"Kill the fuckin' light!"

She snapped it off.

"How come the one who's followin' you's got no light?"

"Doesn't need it. That one's bad news, Dog. Your sentries give him a tumble, they'll come home in easy-to-carry sections."

"This a *friend* friend, Moll?" He sounded uneasy. I heard his feet shift on the worn plywood.

"No. But he's mine. And this one," slapping my shoulder, "he's a friend. Got that?"

"Sure," he said, without much enthusiasm, padding to the platform's edge, where the eyebolts were. He began to pluck out some kind of message on the taut cords.

Nighttown spread beneath us like a toy village for rats; tiny windows showed candlelight, with only a few harsh, bright squares lit by battery lanterns and carbide lamps. I imagined the old men at their endless games of dominoes, under warm, fat drops of water that fell from wet wash hung out on poles between the plywood shanties. Then I tried to imagine him climbing patiently up through the darkness in his zoris and ugly tourist shirt, bland and unhurried. How was he tracking us?

"Good," said Molly. "He smells us."

"Smoke?" Dog dragged a crumpled pack from his pocket and prized out a flattened cigarette. I squinted at the trademark while he lit it for me with a kitchen match. Yiheyuan filters. Beijing Cigarette Factory. I decided that the Lo Teks were black marketeers. Dog and Molly went back to their argument, which seemed to revolve around Molly's desire to use some particular piece of Lo Tek real estate.

"I've done you a lot of favors, man. I want that floor. And I want the music."

"You're not Lo Tek. . . ."

This must have been going on for the better part of a twisted kilometer, Dog leading us along swaying catwalks and up rope ladders. The Lo Teks leech their webs and huddling places to the city's fabric with thick gobs of epoxy and sleep above the abyss in mesh hammocks. Their country is so attenuated that in places it consists of little more than holds for hands and feet, sawed into geodesic struts.

The Killing Floor, she called it. Scrambling after her, my new Eddie Bax shoes slipping on worn metal and damp plywood, I wondered how it could be any more lethal than the rest of the territory. At the same time I sensed that Dog's protests were ritual and that she already expected to get whatever it was she wanted.

Somewhere beneath us, Jones would be circling his tank, feeling the first twinges of junk sickness. The police would be boring the Drome regulars with questions about Ralfi. What did he do? Who was he with before he stepped outside? And the Yakuza would be settling its ghostly bulk over the city's data banks, probing for faint images of me reflected in numbered accounts, securities transactions, bills for utilities. We're an information economy. They teach you that in school. What they don't tell you is that it's impossible to move, to live, to operate at any level without leaving traces, bits, seemingly meaningless fragments of personal information. Fragments that can be retrieved, amplified . . .

But by now the pirate would have shuttled our message into line for blackbox transmission to the Yakuza comsat. A simple message: Call off the dogs or we wideband your program.

The program. I had no idea what it contained. I still don't. I only sing the song, with zero comprehension. It was probably research data, the Yakuza being given to advanced forms of industrial espionage. A genteel business, stealing from Ono-Sendai as a matter of course and politely holding their data for ransom, threatening to blunt the conglomerate's research edge by making the product public.

But why couldn't any number play? Wouldn't they be happier with something to sell back to Ono-Sendai, happier than they'd be with one dead Johnny from Memory Lane?

Their program was on its way to an address in Sydney, to a

place that held letters for clients and didn't ask questions once you'd paid a small retainer. Fourth-class surface mail. I'd erased most of the other copy and recorded our message in the resulting gap, leaving just enough of the program to identify it as the real thing.

My wrist hurt. I wanted to stop, to lie down, to sleep. I knew that I'd lose my grip and fall soon, knew that the sharp black shoes I'd bought for my evening as Eddie Bax would lose their purchase and carry me down to Nighttown. But he rose in my mind like a cheap religious hologram, glowing, the enlarged chip on his Hawaiian shirt looming like a reconnaissance shot of some doomed urban nucleus.

So I followed Dog and Molly through Lo Tek heaven, jury-rigged and jerry-built from scraps that even Nighttown didn't want.

The Killing Floor was eight meters on a side. A giant had threaded steel cable back and forth through a junkyard and drawn it all taut. It creaked when it moved, and it moved constantly, swaying and bucking as the gathering Lo Teks arranged themselves on the shelf of plywood surrounding it. The wood was silver with age, polished with long use and deeply etched with initials, threats, declarations of passion. This was suspended from a separate set of cables, which lost themselves in darkness beyond the raw white glare of the two ancient floods suspended above the Floor.

A girl with teeth like Dog's hit the Floor on all fours. Her breasts were tattooed with indigo spirals. Then she was across the Floor, laughing, grappling with a boy who was drinking dark liquid from a liter flask.

Lo Tek fashion ran to scars and tattoos. And teeth. The electricity they were tapping to light the Killing Floor seemed to be an exception to their overall aesthetic, made in the name of . . . ritual, sport, art? I didn't know, but I could see that the Floor was something special. It had the look of having been assembled over generations.

I held the useless shotgun under my jacket. Its hardness and heft were comforting, even though I had no more shells. And it came to me that I had no idea at all of what was really happening, or of what was supposed to happen. And that was the nature of my game, because I'd spent most of my life as a blind receptacle to be filled with other people's knowledge and then drained, spouting synthetic languages I'd never understand. A very technical boy. Sure.

And then I noticed just how quiet the Lo Teks had become.

He was there, at the edge of the light, taking in the Killing Floor and the gallery of silent Lo Teks with a tourist's calm. And as our eyes met for the first time with mutual recognition, a memory clicked into place for me, of Paris, and the long Mercedes electrics gliding through the rain to Notre Dame; mobile greenhouses, Japanese faces behind the glass, and a hundred Nikons rising in blind phototropism, flowers of steel and crystal. Behind his eyes, as they found me, those same shutters whirring.

I looked for Molly Millions, but she was gone.

The Lo Teks parted to let him step up onto the bench. He bowed, smiling, and stepped smoothly out of his sandals, leaving them side by side, perfectly aligned, and then he stepped down onto the Killing Floor. He came for me, across that shifting trampoline of scrap, as easily as any tourist padding across synthetic pile in any featureless hotel.

Molly hit the Floor, moving.

The Floor screamed.

It was miked and amplified, with pickups riding the four fat coil springs at the corners and contact mikes taped at random to rusting machine fragments. Somewhere the Lo Teks had an amp and a synthesizer, and now I made out the shapes of speakers overhead, above the cruel white floods.

A drumbeat began, electronic, like an amplified heart, steady as a metronome.

She'd removed her leather jacket and boots; her T-shirt was sleeveless, faint telltales of Chiba City circuitry traced along her thin arms. Her leather jeans gleamed under the floods. She began to dance.

She flexed her knees, white feet tensed on a flattened gas tank, and the Killing Floor began to heave in response. The sound it made was like a world ending, like the wires that hold heaven snapping and coiling across the sky.

He rode with it, for a few heartbeats, and then he moved, judging the movement of the Floor perfectly, like a man stepping from one flat stone to another in an ornamental garden.

He pulled the tip from his thumb with the grace of a man at ease with social gesture and flung it at her. Under the floods, the filament was a refracting thread of rainbow. She threw herself flat and rolled, jackknifing up as the molecule whipped past, steel claws snapping into the light in what must have been an automatic rictus of defense.

The drum pulse quickened, and she bounced with it, her dark hair wild around the blank silver lenses, her mouth thin, lips taut with concentration. The Killing Floor boomed and roared, and the Lo Teks were screaming their excitement.

He retracted the filament to a whirling meter-wide circle of ghostly polychrome and spun it in front of him, thumbless hand held level with his sternum. A shield.

And Molly seemed to let something go, something inside, and that was the real start of her mad-dog dance. She jumped, twisting, lunging sideways, landing with both feet on an alloy engine block wired directly to one of the coil springs. I cupped my hands over my ears and knelt in a vertigo of sound, thinking Floor and benches were on their way down, down to Nighttown, and I saw us tearing through the shanties, the wet wash, exploding on the tiles like rotten fruit. But the cables held, and the Killing Floor rose and fell like a crazy metal sea. And Molly danced on it.

And at the end, just before he made his final cast with the filament, I saw something in his face, an expression that didn't seem to belong there. It wasn't fear and it wasn't anger. I think it was disbelief, stunned incomprehension mingled with pure aesthetic revulsion at what he was seeing, hearing—at what was happening to him. He retracted the whirling filament, the ghost disk shrinking to the size of a dinner plate as he whipped his arm above his head and brought it down, the thumbtip curving out for Molly like a live thing.

The Floor carried her down, the molecule passing just above her head; the Floor whiplashed, lifting him into the path of the taut molecule. It should have passed harmlessly over his head and been withdrawn into its diamond-hard socket. It took his hand off just behind the wrist. There was a gap in the Floor in front of him, and he went through it like a diver, with a strange deliberate grace, a defeated kamikaze on his way down to Nighttown. Partly, I think, he took the dive to buy himself a few seconds of the dignity of silence. She'd killed him with culture shock.

The Lo Teks roared, but someone shut the amplifier off, and Molly rode the Killing Floor into silence, hanging on now, her face white and blank, until the pitching slowed and there was only a faint pinging of tortured metal and the grating of rust on rust.

We searched the Floor for the severed hand, but we never found it. All we found was a graceful curve in one piece of rusted steel, where the molecule went through. Its edge was bright as new chrome.

We never learned whether the Yakuza had accepted our terms, or even whether they got our message. As far as I know, their program is still waiting for Eddie Bax on a shelf in the back room of a gift shop on the third level of Sydney Central-5. Probably they sold the original back to Ono-Sendai months ago. But maybe they did get the pirate's broadcast, because nobody's come looking for me yet, and it's been nearly a year. If they do come, they'll have a long climb up through the dark, past Dog's sentries, and I don't look much like Eddie Bax these days. I let Molly take care of that, with a local anesthetic. And my new teeth have almost grown in.

I decided to stay up here. When I looked out across the Killing Floor, before he came, I saw how hollow I was. And I knew I was sick of being a bucket. So now I climb down and visit Jones, almost every night.

We're partners now, Jones and I, and Molly Millions, too. Molly handles our business in the Drome. Jones is still in Funland, but he has a bigger tank, with fresh seawater trucked in once a week. And he has his junk, when he needs it. He still talks to the kids with his frame of lights, but he talks to me on a new display unit in a shed that I rent there, a better unit than the one he used in the navy.

And we're all making good money, better money than I made before, because Jones's Squid can read the traces of anything that anyone ever stored in me, and he gives it to me on the display unit in languages I can understand. So we're learning a lot about all my former clients. And one day I'll have a surgeon dig all the silicon out of my amygdalae, and I'll live with my own memories and nobody else's, the way other people do. But not for a while.

In the meantime it's really okay up here, way up in the dark, smoking a Chinese filtertip and listening to the condensation that drips from the geodesics. Real quiet up here—unless a pair of Lo Teks decide to dance on the Killing Floor.

It's educational, too. With Jones to help me figure things out, I'm getting to be the most technical boy in town.